To Tom,

Best Wishes &
happy Reading

Marc Francis

# Journal of a Husband

# Marc Francis

# Journal of a Husband

Olympia Publishers
*London*

**www.olympiapublishers.com**
OLYMPIA PAPERBACK EDITION

A CIP catalogue record for this title is
available from the British Library.

ISBN: 978-1-80074-347-2

This is a work of fiction.
Names, characters, places and incidents originate from the writer's
imagination. Any resemblance to actual persons, living or dead, is
purely coincidental.

First Published in 2022

Olympia Publishers
Tallis House
2 Tallis Street
London
EC4Y 0AB
Printed in Great Britain

# Dedication

Dedicated to Kelly, my Love.

# "Girl with the green hair"

Before I begin, I want to state for the record that I love coffee. My main fuel source is caffeine, and my god, I have a lot of it. I NEED it, and without it, my Bruce Banner starts to convulse, bulge, turn a distinct shade of green and I feel the need tear my shirt open.

I did try to stop my caffeine intake completely once, I lasted about two hours. After about half an hour, I thought "this is easy", but it was all downhill from there. Within moments I resembled the Duracell bunny when the guy on the advert puts in the shitty competitor batteries. I came to a complete standstill, and if I had been carrying a drum (like the Duracell bunny) I would have been slumped over it.

OK, so I have made it clear that coffee is something I rely on heavily. So, you would think that when the caffeine levels in my system drop, and I am out and about with wife, I would be more than happy to throw the doors open of my local Starbucks and replenish my great need for the brown bean. Well... You'd be WRONG. Let me elaborate.

Picture the scene, it's approaching eleven thirty a.m. Wife and I are in town "shopping" on a piss wet Saturday morning (anyone under thirty will probably find this an alien concept, as it involves physically traveling to real shops, in a real town).

Anyway, I had been following the wife for two hours, and as I conclude my rant about the death of the high street (which I will cover in another chapter. But essentially, unless you want to obtain a payday loan, use some of the money to buy a kebab, buy a fruity e-cig, pick the winner of the two forty-five at Haydock or throw what's left of your loan into the flat cap of a really shit accordion player with a near dead dog, then the high street is not for you. Also, don't forget to keep the majority of your loan aside to pay for the car park.)

My wife throws me a lifeline, "Shall we go for a coffee?"

My instant reaction of "Yeah, great" is fuelled by my reliance on caffeine, and also my desire not to be piss wet through.

I notice my wife has made a move towards a door, and as I look up, I see the sign, the woman with the green hair.

Yes, it's Starbucks. The Seattle based coffee steam roller that has turned enjoying a relaxing cup of coffee in relative peace, into an overcrowded gathering of laptop laden wi-fi seeking pretentious wankers.

When you do manage to eventually get served, and financially raped at the till (but don't worry, you get chocolate sprinkles) you have to decipher the hieroglyphs that are scrawled in sharpie vertically on the side of your cup which is meant to be your name (that you provided to the zombie on the till when handing over vast amounts of money).

As we join the back of the enormous queue, my wife asks, "What shall I have?"

At Starbucks, you are greeted with this mind-boggling decision...

Cereal latte with dairy free oat
Cafe Latte
Iced Cafe Latte
Flat white
Latte with Turmeric (WTF!)
White Chocolate Mocha
Iced White Chocolate Mocha
Cafe Mocha
Iced Cafe Mocha
Latte Macchiato
Caramel Macchiato
Iced Caramel Macchiato
Classic Iced Cappuccino
Cold foam Iced Cappuccino
Cappuccino
Caffe Americano
Iced Caffe Americano
Cortado (no, not a clue either)
Espresso
Espresso Con Panna
Espresso Macchiato
Cold Brew
Cold Brew Latte
Nitro cold brew
Nitro with cold foam
Nitro with caramel cold foam
Cafe Misto
Mini Java Chip Frappuccino
Caramel Frappuccino

Mini Coffee Frappuccino
Coffee Frappuccino
Mini Espresso Frappuccino
Java Chip Frappuccino
Mini Caramel Frappuccino
Mini Mocha Frappuccino
Espresso Frappuccino
Mocha Frappuccino
White Chocolate Mocha Frappuccino (say that when your pissed)
Mini White Chocolate Mocha Frappuccino
Mini Strawberries and Cream Frappuccino
Chai Cream Frappuccino
Mini Chai Cream Frappuccino
Caramel Cream Frappuccino
Matcha Green tea Creme Frappuccino
Mini Matcha Green tea Crème Frappuccino
Mini Caramel Cream Frappuccino
Mini Vanilla Cream Frappuccino
Double chocolate Chip Frappuccino
White Chocolate cream Frappuccino
Caramel Light Frappuccino
Coffee Light Frappuccino
Espresso Light Frappuccino
Mocha Light Frappuccino
White Chocolate Mocha Light Frappuccino
Java Chip Light Frappuccino
Mango Passion fruit Frappuccino
AND... Freshly Brewed Coffee! (I kid you not.)

It is impossible for any sane human being to make an informed decision when faced with this immense list.

What most of these idiots in here do is pretend they know what they have ordered. They don't.

By the time they peel their eyes from their mobiles, having shuffled to the front of the line, they panic, and one of two things occurs. Firstly, some will try and sound like they know what they are doing, and order something that will sound impressive, "I'll have a Latte Macchiato" (Wanker). I guarantee they have no fucking idea what a "Macchiato" is.

Then others will look for a familiar word in the vast menu i.e., "Caramel" or "Chocolate" so they can place a safe bet. This is why some of these concoctions resemble desserts that should have a sparkler in them. Case in point…

I mean COME ON! This looks like a care bear has vomited in a cup. You see, these establishments have no interest in customers like me, I want a coffee. Strong, black, no sugar, in a real cup.

Now, I have no issue with people drinking these ridiculously expensive vile creations, but please don't call yourself a COFFEE shop, because coffee drinkers (like myself) just want a quality COFFEE at a fair price.

Now, Wife and I have finally reached the front of the line, and Wife has selected her "coffee" from the menu.

"Hi, what can I get you?" asks our overworked barista (yeah, right).

"Please can I have a double chocolate chip Frappuccino," says Wife. (Great, one of the most expensive drinks I have ever seen)

"Small, Tall, Grande or Venti?" asks Mr Starbucks.

Now this refers to the size of screwing you are about

to receive.

"Venti, please," Wife replies. (The Biggest. Naturally, I would have put all I own on this response)

Now, as Mr Starbucks starts to tap our order into the machine that will financially bugger me, the question comes, that quite honestly astounded me.

"Would you like coffee in that?" Mr "Barista" (a "COFFEE" technician) asks.

Did I hear right? Do you want coffee in it? Did I imagine that question?

"No thanks," Wife replies.

My jaw is well and truly open at this stage as Mr Starbucks taps away. And, the questions keep coming.

"Whipped Cream?" asks Mr Starbucks.

"Yes, please" Wife enthuses.

"Chocolate Syrup?" asks Mr Starbucks.

"Yes please," replies wife (what a shock).

I actually thought he was going to ask if Wife would like a balloon or some crayons when the questions stop. Mr Starbucks turns his attention to me.

"Please can I have a freshly brewed coffee?" I proclaim.

It feels like time has stopped. For what seems like an age, there is silence, even Wife seems embarrassed. Even the laptop tapping has stopped throughout the building. Mr Starbucks looks at me like I have just asked him to serve me a freshly slaughtered Panda cub.

"Err, yes," Mr Starbucks finally replies.

"What…"

"Small," I reply before he has time to compose himself.

"No syrup, sugar, whipped cream, milk (almond, coconut, soy, blah blah blah) or anything else," I say proudly.

"OK," says Mr Starbucks, as he bites his bottom lip while he genuinely struggles to find the right buttons to press for my ultra-rare order on the rape machine.

When Mr Starbucks asks for our names (for his sharpie scrawlings on our cups) and then brings up our bill (which costs the same as a good night out when I was nineteen) we are ushered to the end of the Starbucks conveyor belt to await our drinks.

As the staff frantically prepare our drinks, other expectant customers stand around waiting for their creations. As each drink is passed on to the server, they then have to attempt to read the hastily scrawled name in Sharpie on the side of each cup.

These names are written vertically on each cup, which results in server and customer attempting to read the name by cocking their head to one side. One by one, each person is given their "coffee" once their names are deciphered on their cup, and they disappear into the street, or stand around attempting to find a non-existent seat.

Wife has been issued with her abomination, as I wait for mine. Finally, an offering appears that resembles a cup which actually contains coffee and nothing else.

As Miss Starbucks cocks her head to one side, in an attempt to read what must be my name, I say…

"That must be mine."

"Oh OK, I thought it was a mistake. It's just a coffee"

I take my coffee in a defiant manner, and we hit the

streets to renew our shopping excursion.

I drink my coffee as fast as the temperature allows me to, and as I do, I notice the Sharpie scrawl on the side of the cup. Even though no one could ever be sure of what it says, Wife asks…

"Why have they written 'Weirdo' on your cup?"

# IKEA Part 1 "Black Wednesday"

I can feel myself tense up when I hear the wife utter the words, "Are you off work on Wednesday?"

I can feel my stomach starting to churn as I think to myself, "She fucking well knows I am."

I realise that any notion of rest and relaxation are hanging by a thread ready to be cut by one of her thirty pairs of scissors that reside inexplicably in the cutlery draw, causing the drawer to simply refuse to close without the technical assistance of NASA.

After what to her must seem like an age, I muster the courage to reply.

"Yes, that's right Wednesday... why?"

I hold my breath.

"Just checking." (Bullshit, there's ALWAYS a reason.)

Here it comes...

"It's just..."

As the wife utters the words, I peer into the hall to realise my worst fears. Emerging from the cupboard under the stairs, her arse shuffles backwards into the light, followed by (please God, no) the colour scheme every sane human fears (every man that is). Yellow? Blue handle? Oh, fuck me, no... it's the IKEA bags!

"No fucking way! I'm not going to sodding IKEA!" I proclaim, knowing I would definitely be going.

"It'll be quiet on a Wednesday!" the wife declares.

TIME OUT. At this point, I feel the need to cut through some of the IKEA propaganda. I want to make it clear to every husband, boyfriend and fellow male on the planet reading this. If you ever hear the words, "it'll be quiet" in relation to IKEA, "YOU ARE BEING LIED TO!" It is NEVER QUIET.

Quiet to me, is where you can move your trolley freely without the fear of severing the Achilles tendon of the Scouser, or OAP (or worse still, a Scouse OAP) in front of you.

Quiet to me, is not having to dive off the arrow led human train that snakes it ways through the seemingly never-ending mile after mile of Swedish hell, so you can view a product without having to break one of the IKEA Commandments, "THOU SHALL ALWAYS WALK IN THE DIRECTION OF THE ARROWS!"

If you are new to domestic bliss and are about to embark on your first IKEA experience, I feel duty bound to tell my fellow comrades the truth, everything you have been told by your other half is a LIE!

Anyway, back to my account.

"Quiet! Are you fucking kidding me!" My hands are waving in the air at this point.

"What do we need?"

This question is irrelevant, as I know we NEED fuck all.

"Glasses... artificial flowers... And err... cushions."

At this point, I am fantasising about placing the IKEA bag over Wife's head until she stops twitching.

"They're cheap! Oh, go on, I will buy you some meatballs." At this point she is giving me those eyes, and clutching the IKEA bags to her chest.

There are a couple of things to pick up on here in this statement. Firstly, it is true to say that items in IKEA are indeed "cheap", but you will spend a bastard fortune and you won't understand how.

It is probably due to the fact that the store is the size of Stockholm, and the cumulative effect of being exposed to six billion "cheap" products means you will spend a cocking mint!

Secondly, the female during the persuasion process will try and seal the deal using what I call the "meatball curveball". Those of you who are new to IKEA, I will explain.

They have a cafe halfway round the Stockholm— sorry "store" (usually situated about four miles into your pilgrimage) which sells meals at ridiculously cheap prices. Their most famous offering is their Swedish meatballs, with a redcurrant jelly.

Sounds good? Don't be fooled. As a hardened IKEA Veteran, this Scandanavian culinary silver lining to the IKEA cloud is a big con, and I will explain my reasons later.

Sorry, I digress.

"We'll go early. We will drop the kids off at school, and go straight there. You know, beat the traffic." Wife leaves the conversation, and the room before I am able to protest further.

"Whoopee fucking doo," I manage to mutter while launching the indestructible IKEA bag down the hall.

# IKEA Part 2 "The Visit"

Wednesday

Well, today's the day. Today I am being subjected to the Swedish nightmare that is IKEA. As I try to prepare myself psychologically while sipping my first coffee of the day, Wife is skipping around the kitchen like it's Christmas.

As I pack the kids into the car, travel mug in hand, Wife is bouncing up and down in the passenger seat like Tigger.

On the journey to school, I peer into the rear view mirror periodically to the sight of my eldest smirking at me, he knows what I am in for.

I divert my gaze to my youngest who just looks at me with concern.

As I pull up to the school gates, Wife couldn't get the kids out of car quick enough. It was like watching a kidnapping in reverse. The "Hi Vis" vest wearing woman at the gates, whose job it is to marshal the kids into school safely (who actually spends the entire time gathering gossip from slipper wearing, makeup less mothers) just stares mouth open, as our kids land on the pavement.

"OK, go, go!" Wife says. And with that, we are IKEA Bound.

We are close, I can see the blue and yellow flags in the distance slowly getting larger as we approach. Wife has spent the entire journey mapping out her strategy for our visit with military precision, but honestly, I haven't listened to a single word.

"WELCOME TO IKEA" the sign proclaims, as I turn into the vast no man's land between freedom and Swedish hell they call "Car Park".

Finding a car parking space at IKEA is nigh on impossible, despite the car park being the size of Wales.

As I drive up and down the seemingly never-ending rows of parked cars (while religiously abiding by the IKEA law of following the arrows) I observe others at various stages of their torment.

There are people like us, searching for a space that doesn't exist, red faced sweating husbands who look like they are walking on the deck of a capsizing ship as they attempt to somehow push their ridiculously overloaded flatpack laden trolleys to their cars while their wives study their two foot long receipts.

I notice Wife's head is slowly looking left to right, like Arnie in the Terminator scanning for his next target.

"There's one! Quick!" Wife shrieks.

I accelerate violently, swing the car dangerously in front of many pedestrians (at this stage, I don't give a shit) and finally manage to bring the car to a halt.

Wife reaches for the IKEA bags in a state of renewed excitement, and we both manage to squeeze out of the car in our ridiculously tight parking space.

"There, told you it would be quiet," Wife decrees.

We couldn't have parked further away if we had tried, we are literally light years from the store. You can always tell how far away you are because there is always that single, rusty three-wheeled trolley dumped in a hedge.

After what seemed like an age, and after crossing two time zones, we converge on the huge revolving doors, with all the other poor bastards, which ushers you into the store with what should be a certain level of efficiency.

At this point, I feel the need to address my feelings regarding revolving doors. In theory, they are a great idea.

However, apply the delirious over excitement of Wife (and countless other wives) about to enter "IKEALAND", it all goes fucking pear shaped.

As the revolving door, well... revolves, each space designed to transport you from the real world to Scandinavian mayhem opens, which allows you to enter and shuffle round until your exit space opens to allow you to start your flatpack fuckery.

Easy, right? Noooooooo. What happens is this: over eager individuals (usually Wife) feels the need to pack the revolving door space to the point where (yes, you guessed it) somebody at the front or the back touches the door, and the whole thing fucking stops!

You are then stuck, albeit momentarily, staring at the other thirty people in a space designed for four, trying to decide who committed the cardinal sin of touching the door. Is it the thirty stone woman in the mobility scooter, which is the same size as my first car? Or one of the wives foaming at the mouth, who are unable to control themselves for five seconds. My money is usually on the parent who feels the need to push their child's double buggy through the revolving door experience for no logical reason.

One thing is for sure, I am not responsible for this. Due to the fact, guess what, I choose to use a cocking door!

Anyway, we're in, and with IKEA bag in hand, Wife races to the escalator to find her first arrow to follow.

As we make our climb on the escalator, I turn to look down at the ongoing revolving door chaos behind us, the line for the creche (which I must admit, if I could pass as a two year old, I would gladly sneak my way in, and spend the next three hours inserting Lego in my nose and soiling myself, rather than finding the first arrow) and the queue for the elevator, which consists of anyone who isn't able bodied or has chosen to bring a tank sized pram with them.

So it begins, we join the human arrow following train, snaking its way through the seemingly never ending display rooms designed to make you feel terrible about your own home, and to make you believe you can make your living room look like a Manhattan apartment for the price of loaf of bread.

"Ooo, I like this," Wife says for the five hundredth time.

At this point, my account gets a bit fuzzy, most of my senses have shut down to a point where my brain has maintained just enough activity to stop me falling over or dribbling.

I do remember locking eyes with a fellow male sufferer at some point, who was also with his wife. Even though our brains were in a near vegetative state, as our eyes locked, I could have sworn I saw a tear.

Bag one is now full, I don't know what with, but it's

full. As we make our way round yet another corner, one of my senses that shutdown two hours ago springs to life, my sense of smell.

Yes, the IKEA cafe comes into view, and I want to cry.

I actually think I started skipping, but I can't be sure. I touched on what I call the "meatball curve ball" in part one, which is nearly always used in the persuasion stage, to get husband through the revolving door in the first place with the promise IKEA's famous meatballs.

The ecstasy I felt at the sight of the cafe, started to subside very quickly as I entered this oasis. I think at that moment, the entire English speaking world were queuing for meatballs.

I was devastated, I could have eaten the child in the enormous pram in front of me, but her mother was watching.

Having joined the back of the queue with my plastic tray, I surveyed the scene in front of me, it was chaos. While wife was on the IKEA website on her phone (no doubt planning the 2nd leg of our tour) the pram park was overflowing, every chair and flat surface that was capable of being sat on was occupied.

"Shall we just crack on, and get something to eat later?" Wife asked.

If my tray would've had a sharp edge, I would have used it.

"NO FUCKING WAY?" I barked.

"I want meatballs, that was the deal," I reminded Wife.

"OK, but look at the queue."

Wife was right, I could see in the distance people serving scoop after scoop of meatballs to the masses, and we were hardly moving.

After what seemed like hours (probably ten minutes) I was at my breaking point. If I had to watch one more individual walk past me with their tray of food on their way to find a non-existent seat, I will end their life.

It was no good, we were getting nowhere. The final straw came when an IKEA employee approached, and a hastily scrawled message on the chalkboard next to me confirmed my worst fears...

"Sorry, we have sold out of meatballs."

Wife looked at me and was convinced I was having a stroke.

"Are you OK? Come on, I will buy you a hotdog on the way out," Wife says.

If you are still enjoying your IKEALAND virginity, you will be blissfully unaware that IKEA has a small shop on the way out of their stores where you can buy a multitude of IKEA products (including fucking meatballs, although frozen) and also ridiculously cheap hot dogs and coffee.

Knowing I was still in for a for a ridiculously long wait, I reluctantly agree. My final act was to discreetly give the fingers to the kid in the enormous pram that I considered eating in front of me.

Wife was ecstatic that we had re-joined the arrow trail, and I returned to my near vegetative state.

After bag number two reached capacity, Wife and I entered the final area, where lies rack after rack of flatpacks. This is where you collect your enormous boxes and load them onto your trolley. Thankfully, I was spared this ordeal today, but I am a hardened veteran and feel the pain of my fellow wheezing husbands trying to manoeuvre these monster loads.

"Daylight!" I proclaim, just a little too loudly. As Wife goes through the tills, I perch on a display chair, and feel what a £29 chair feels like. To be honest, at this stage, I would have sat on a spike. It actually felt like it was made in the wood shop by an inmate at HMP Strangeways who was high on spice.

We are nearly there. I can see the world beyond IKEALAND, and I want it.

Wife is through the tills, Wife has been issued with her two-foot-long receipt, and I gladly leave the world's most uncomfortable chair behind for the next husband.

"RIGHT! Hotdog." Nothing will stop me.

From a great distance, I make and hold eye contact with the guy at the shop who also doubles up as the guy serving coffee and hotdogs. He looks positively terrified as I bear down on him.

I reach the front of the serving area for the hotdogs straight away, no queue! However, I still have to wait while he finishes serving a woman at the shop till who is buying frozen meatballs (Bitch). It seems like an eternity, and I started to countdown in my head from ten.

If this woman does not find the coins in her purse by the time I reach zero, I have vowed to beat her to death with a frozen dime cake (very nice by the way) in the freezer next to her.

I reach two in my countdown when the guy I am eyeballing issues her with her receipt.

*Finally!* I thought as he turns to serve me my hot dog.

"How can I help you?" said Darren. His name, according to his badge.

"Darren, I would like a hot dog," I said proudly.

"Sorry we've sold out." Darren informed me.

Darren started to look scared, as whatever expression I had on my face, obviously made Darren very uncomfortable.

"SOLD OUT!"

The volume of my response prompted Wife to come over and to momentarily stop examining her receipt.

"Oh dear, let's go. We can grab something on the way home," said Wife.

Darren was saved. Wife had intervened at the perfect moment, and prevented Darren from being hospitalised.

As I breathe in my first breath of freedom (non IKEALAND air) en route to the car, I can't help but pity the still never-ending flow of husbands being led by their wives, approaching the revolving door with the promise of non-existing meatballs. I want to shout out and tell them about the false promise of meatballs, but I can't. If I did, there would be carnage.

As Wife and I leave the car park (being careful to avoid the three wheeled trolley sticking out of the hedge) I can still hear the following volleys of swear words on the wind from husbands trying to fit a nine-foot flat pack box in their Ford Fiesta.

"I told you it wouldn't fucking fit!" he shrieks. That's the sound of a man who hasn't had his meatballs.

# "Who has the time?"

OK, so by now you have probably realised certain things in life annoy me (who would have guessed?). Now, what should annoy me, are things that most people feel annoyed about.

Things like social injustice, world hunger and/or our self-inflicted damage to the environment. Or in the case of Wife, who is going to be the next orange, bird-brained, socialite-wannabe with blindingly white teeth voted off "Love Island". You get the picture.

Now, in my case there is an issue I have which I simply cannot let go of, no matter how hard I try. If this annoyance was a politician, it would be fired for not doing its job, it would be hauled before the courts for lying and be accused of conspiring to mislead the electorate.

I am of course referring that lying little digital bastard that is the microwave clock. It is undoubtedly one of life's enduring mysteries. Firstly, why the fuck do you need a clock on the microwave in the first place? I mean, I have never thought, "I wonder what time it is?" while watching last night's pizza rotating round, reaching a near volcanic temperature.

Secondly, it is easier to perform open heart surgery while severely drunk and high on mushrooms than get this little fucking LCD screen to tell the truth.

After moving into our house twelve months ago, I have had to endure this little integrated fucker flaunt it's flashing display at me every time I enter the kitchen as if to say, "Your no man, I defy you."

If this rebellious appliance hadn't been integrated and simply sat on the counter, I would've ended its life by now. I have often fantasised about taking a baseball bat to it, or ejecting it from the third floor window a la Keith Richards style. However, it knows it's here to stay and it therefore feels it has the upper hand.

Anyway, recently I reached a watershed moment. It had flashed the wrong time to me once too often. It had undermined my authority for too long. I snapped, it was time to act... I am going to SET the microwave clock ONCE and for ALL!

I needed a plan. Wife could tell that something was happening when she caught me sifting through THE drawer. You know, the one with every receipt, recipe, magazine clipping, used battery, elastic band and key (that you don't know what it's for but are too scared to throw away "just in case").

"What are you doing? You're making a mess," Wife barks.

"Making a mess! Are you kidding? This fucking drawer is like Mary Poppins carpet bag."

I calm myself momentarily.

"I am looking for the instructions for the microwave. That little bastard is getting it!"

"Getting It? Getting what?" Wife looks genuinely concerned.

"It's taken the piss out of me once too often, I am

GOING to set the microwave clock!"

Wife could see my determination, and she realised I meant business. She looked terrified.

"I don't think we ever had them; I don't remember seeing them. You might have to forget it." Wife was trying to pull me back from the brink.

"No! I will just have to fly blind," I said defiantly, while slamming the "THE" drawer and causing a Tsunami of dead batteries which crashed into the cupboard below.

"I will leave you to it then," Wife said as she retreated to relative safety.

"OK, it's just you and me," I said to the microwave as we stared each other down.

I embarked on a frenzied, randomised sequence of button pressing which resulted in me finding out how to defrost various weights of poultry, perfectly prepare vegetables and combine grilling with all the speed and convenience of microwaving. However, still NOTHING even remotely close to indicating how to set the fucking time.

After what seemed like days (actually around a couple of hours), I was on the brink of accepting the microwave had got me where it wanted me, when I threw a last volley of button abuse it's way.

Suddenly, without warning the display flashed in a way I had not seen before. What's this? I thought as this letter sequence started to appear C… L … O… C… K.

I could feel the tears rolling down my face as I realised I had reached the promised land. After carefully setting the hour and minutes, I pressed the final button to save my achievement.

There it was, the microwave clock had been conquered. It read 21:26, and it was RIGHT.

I wanted to mark the occasion, so I summoned the children to the kitchen and also shouted for Wife to come through and see what her husband had done.

"Well, boys, what do you think?" I said proudly.

"What am I looking at?" my eldest remarked.

"Your father has successfully set the microwave clock!" I was awaiting my congratulatory hug and praise.

"Jesus," eldest said as he shuffled out of the kitchen with my youngest in tow who couldn't even manage to utter a word.

I resumed gazing at the microwave in awe, when Wife finally enters the kitchen while reading something in her hand.

"Ahhh, you managed it then?" Wife said sympathetically.

"Yes, look at it," I said, as I notice her still fixed on the booklet in hand.

"I was going to come through and tell you, but Love Island was on."

"Tell me what?" I asked while still riding my wave.

"I found this in "THE" drawer, look at page eight," she said as she hands me the booklet.

It read, "How to set your microwave clock in three easy steps"

At that moment I could have sworn I heard the microwave chuckling, as I wonder how much damage I could do if I filled my sock with all those used batteries.

# "Romance is Dead"

OK, I want to be clear about the title of this chapter. When I say, "Romance is dead", I don't mean farting violently in front of Wife, and looking positively proud. Or leaving one's destroyed underwear on the bedroom floor, or even leaving my pubic hair deeply tangled in Wife's lady razor.

What I actually mean is that romance and memory shouldn't mix. Romantic childhood memories lead to all sorts of disappointments, frustrations and lies. And I feel the need to WARN YOU ALL!

The fascinating thing about childhood "romantic memory" is that it is all a fucking lie. Your mind literally kids you into thinking the summers used to be blisteringly hot and it never rained, we had barbeques every day and played football (soccer, for any Americanese readers) on the freshly cut green grass until eleven p.m.

In winter, the snow used to be eleven feet deep, we'd make perfect snowmen in the crisp virgin snow, and then we all huddled in front of the coal fire, drinking hot chocolate and telling all our family how much we loved each other.

Also, how Snickers (Marathon for those of a certain age) bars used to be three feet long in 1984, and it took you and two other able-bodied childhood friends to carry it home.

Your lying mind also provides you with the false memory of how far your pocket money (allowance for the Americanese) used to go. Your memory tells you that you could eat sweets (candy for the Americanese) every day for a week, visit the cinema at will, and still have enough left to settle Angola's national debt.

None of it is true, it is all a lie. Your mind has concocted the whole thing, the reality is very, very different.

Firstly, in the summer it rained violently most of the time and rarely scraped above seventeen degrees. If it did creep above this temperature, a strange thing occurred.

People used to literally strip off. Dad would parade around with high cut 1984 Daley Thompson shorts on (you know, were the seam perfectly separates the ball bag down the middle, google it) he'd be bare chested, sporting enormous aviator sunglasses, while smoking an embassy No. 1. He actually thought he was Magnum P.I. (without the Ferrari, he had an Austin Allegro) and he would spend hours like this stood over an ice-cold barbeque applying all sorts of flammable liquids to it, in a vain attempt to create combustion.

Yes, we would spend hours playing football, but the reality was quite different. We would climb over the school fence to play on long grass (not freshly cut) while trying to avoid dog shit of all shades (Why do you never see white dog shit anymore? Weird.) whilst also trying to avoid broken milk bottles.

When I did return home, usually with a huge cut on my knee from a broken bottle, Dad would still be trying to ignite the barbeque so we could eat something.

On this occasion, I remember being sat on the kitchen

counter while Mum was applying the plaster (Americanese translation: "Band aid") to my knee, when I heard a sickening scream from the garden. Mum and I rushed outside to see Dad rolling around on the grass, attempting to extinguish his melting shorts, and the garden fence was a raging inferno. The ash from his Embassy No. 1 must have finally caused ignition. (Mr Leonard, the war veteran across the road said later, he thought the Russians had dropped the bomb)

After putting Dad out using the dishwater, and using the garden hose to put out the fence, Dad stood there in his scorched Y fronts and said, "Chippy it is then."

Winter was no better. Firstly, it never snowed. Like "summer" it rained, but in winter the rain was cold. On the rare (I MEAN rare) occasion it did actually snow, children would stampede outside in their wellies to create frozen dog shit laden slush men, out of the one cm of 'snow'.

Once thoroughly piss wet through, and frozen to near cryogenic levels, I would retreat into the house, strip off my wet clothes and wrap myself up in front of the fire (not coal, but a very 1970s gas fire that would quite often ignite my nylon socks) while drinking a cup of Bovril (not hot chocolate).

So, you see, reality is FAR removed from this false memory narrative.

Now, although I have "awoken" and realised this, Wife still believes in the "romantic memories" from the past. This leads me perfectly into my account of what was to follow.

Every year, from the end of August until November I brace myself for Wife to tell me when our annual visit will occur, to one of my most hated destinations on God's green earth. I am of course talking about "Blackpool Illuminations".

For those of you who are not familiar with this brightly lit hell hole, it is the famous coastal Lancashire town of Blackpool, with its famous tower and annual light show which stretches along a seemingly never-ending coastal road.

Here it comes…

"Shall we go to the Illuminations on Friday?" Wife asks. She's not actually asking; I know we are going.

My heart sinks.

"We can ride the tram, get some rock and fish and chips on the way back," she says, while delving into that "romantic memory" from childhood that is completely removed from reality.

It is futile to resist, so with a heavy heart, I reluctantly agree.

"OK, if you want to," I submit.

Now, the idea of an evening visit to Blackpool, for a traditional seaside trip to enjoy fish and chips, ride a tram and get a stick of rock might sound great, right?

It's not, it is a total nightmare. Let me explain...

We set out on our "trip" at six p.m. as it's getting dark. The kids wanted to go less than I did, so they managed to negotiate a pass to their friends for a furious Xbox session and sleepover (jealous) so it's Wife and I tonight (two less people to fall out with I suppose).

With coffee in hand, we hit the road. We get within ten miles of Blackpool relatively trouble free, and then stop. It looks like Armageddon, and every car in Britain is seemingly visiting Blackpool.

"Ooo, it's busy," Wife says, as I try to calculate if my coffee is still hot enough to scald her.

"Yeah, it's busy," I say. Like I do every year.

After what feels like days, I realise we are getting close, as I spot more cars with Scottish flags on them (my god, the Scots love Blackpool) and a steady flow of inflatable penis filled minibuses with screaming hen parties flashing their tits at unsuspecting motorists.

Finally, after eventually finding a parking space sandwiched between a minibus and another Scottish flag laden car, we head out into the cold.

The first thing we are greeted with is the sight of a "hen" from the minibus parked next to us, vomiting out of the window, as her inflatable penis clings on for dear life.

We eventually find our way to the tram stop, after avoiding even more vomiting hen parties and Scottish alcoholics.

Wife and I finally squeeze onto the tram to take us on our journey of disappointment to view the illuminations. Now, due to the huge amount of drunks and OAP's that have squeezed onto our tram, it has created a problem.

The windows are completely steamed up, therefore we see absolutely NOTHING. We spend the entire journey smelling the stale alcohol, cigarettes and sweat from our fellow patrons against the backdrop of multi coloured steamed up windows.

When we finally arrive back at the tram stop having seen nothing, we disembark and I can see the disappointment on Wife's face. I try to salvage the situation.

"That was nice, wasn't it?"

Wife does not respond. I think she wants to hurt me.

"Come on, we will get some rock," I say optimistically (I am a good liar).

Wife seems to cheer up as we head over to one of the thousands of stalls selling every sugary confection you can imagine. From enormous twelve inch candy cocks, to cherry flavoured edible G-strings (classy), the mind boggles.

As we choose our Rock from the nonsexual organ shaped section, the hen party arrives. They seemed to have made time, between drinking and vomiting, to all buy the largest candy cocks available and proceed to enthusiastically "taste" their cocks.

Any shred of tradition and sentiment disappears as we witness the hen choke on her enormous candy cock.

We hurriedly depart with our rock into the darkness, leaving our Hen to vomit once more.

As we arrive back at the car, I feel sorry for Wife. Her romantic notions of Blackpool have been shattered.

But, here's the thing. She will feel the sting of having the romance of Blackpool shattered, but next year, she won't remember a thing of this visit. The dream and illusion will be restored, and between August and November next year I will be forced to make my return.

As we arrive home, Wife is enjoying her stick of Blackpool rock. I reach for my stick and unwrap it. I notice I must have picked mine from the wrong section.

The phrase running through my rock read:

"Blackpool, fuck you."

I couldn't have put it better myself.

# "Can U Just?"

OK, let me set the scene, I work, a lot. So much in fact, that I have been known to address Wife by my boss's name, and the kids have often mistaken me for a burglar. Now, I don't want a medal, I don't need brownie points, as there are many people across the land who work as hard and longer hours than I do.

The reason I feel the need to make this clear will become apparent. Around six p.m. most nights, while at work, I receive a text message. My joyous skip to my car (knowing my working day is done, and I will soon be in my COMFY clothes, consisting of elasticated trousers, novelty woollen socks and a comfy twenty-year-old jumper, or sweater for my Americanese readers) is obliterated by this vibrating ping from my mobile (cell phone if your Yankish).

Now, ALL I want to do is spend my commute looking forward to removing my shirt and tie, pulling on my COMFY clothes, and taking on the look of a refugee and watching the football (Yankish = soccer) but when I receive the text, I don't even need to read it, I KNOW how it goes.

It's from Wife, and it always starts with… "Can u Just…". Now the rest of the text can consist of anything, and I mean ANYTHING. One thing is for sure, my working day is not done. This text in this case read…

"Can u just stop and pick up some cat litter x"

Now, I appreciate our cats need their litter, but after a ten hour day, I am perfectly at peace with them shitting virtually anywhere: the plants, the oven, but preferably in wife's slippers.

But, resistance is futile. As ALWAYS, I agree to stop on the way home and I cave into wife's demands. I know what you might be thinking, Wife might not drive, SHE DOES, and has her own car. You might think Wife would have to travel miles to reach the nearest supermarket, SHE DOESN'T. In fact, if you stand on your tiptoes at our bedroom window, you can see the too-old-to-work guy collecting trolleys (Yankish = carts) in the car park. In fact, if he wasn't stone deaf, you could shout, "Mind that car!" to him.

But, for some reason, the fact I am already OUT of the house makes me fair game. The act of leaving the house seems to be too monumental of a task for Wife to undertake.

So, as I arrive at the shop (actually, a supermarket but we call it the shop regardless of the fact it is the size of Siberia) and, being careful not to mow down the deaf trolley gatherer, I enter.

Now "The Shop" is a strange place at six forty-five p.m. As you may have gathered at this point, I am quite judgmental (no, really) so, my intention of walking in, picking up reasonably priced cat litter, walking out and going home to dress as a homeless person, quickly turns into something quite different.

As I begin my search for the pet aisle, so I can get the hell home, I end up venturing up and down in my pursuit of the elusive litter.

Firstly, my attention is drawn to a man as I pass the medicine and cosmetics. Now, not because he is hovering around the sanitary towels and thrush cream, but because he is wearing fucking SHORTS! Not a crime I hear you say, and you'd be right, it wasn't minus two degrees outside.

What is it with some men? No matter the weather, they wake up in the morning, look out of the window at their frozen car windscreen, and say, "Yep, cargo shorts today!" WTF!

It makes no sense. This guy's penis must have retreated quicker than the french army when they hear it's two for one at the local brothel. His cock will currently resemble a walnut whip (a particular childhood favourite, no, not men's cocks, the chocolate confection).

It must be a macho thing, but it's not, he looks like a complete tosser. What makes it stranger, from the waist up he is suitably attired. He is wearing a thick jumper and body warmer (Yankish = Gilet) but from the waist down his legs are turning blue. I must admit to lingering longer in this aisle to observe his strange behaviour.

Why is he gazing at various types of vaginal lubrication solutions? I know exactly why. You see, I have observed this behaviour many times before in this particular area of many "shops". This man is attempting to buy CONDOMS (bizarre, considering his penis has deserted him). Let me elaborate.

You see, men are terrified of buying condoms. They will spend inexplicable amounts of time waiting for the optimum moment to strike and reach for their ribbed rubber prey. Next time you see a man for the second time down the medicine aisle in thirty seconds, observe. He is stalking his prey, by repeatedly pacing the medicine aisle and pretending to be interested in cough syrup. Once the aisle is clear, he will pounce and make a grab for his pleasure domes.

As I watch from the end of the aisle, our blue legged friend follows the behaviour perfectly. He makes his final approach, not knowing I am watching, and with no one else in sight, he snatches the box and tucks it under his broccoli in his basket, and he departs for home. Hopefully, he can lure his penis back into the light with his purchase.

My "Can u Just" cat litter pursuit continues, and after exploring another square mile, I am greeted by a crowd. This is of course, the REDUCED section. Now, at this time in the evening, a shop employee begins to apply little yellow reduced price stickers to an array of products.

This causes chaos. Shoppers will scramble to buy enormous quantities of reduced produce they will never consume. No sooner has the terrified employee applied the sticker, a random hand will put six enormous portions of reduced coleslaw (that needs eating by tomorrow) into their overflowing basket. I mean, are they going home to bathe in coleslaw and indulge in some cabbage-based fetish?

It's never ending, twenty boiled eggs, a rainbow trout, a bizarre flavoured purple quiche, four pints of almond milk, a lonely scotch egg and some wrapped up offal without a description. ALL of this must be eaten by tomorrow, and all of this is now piled high in a basket belonging to a woman next to me. As I wander off to locate the cat litter, I wonder what a baked rainbow trout, scotch egg and offal stew in almond milk will taste like.

At last! I finally locate the cat litter. I grab the nearest bag and make a dash for the tills. I am within feet of freedom, when my mobile vibrates. It reads… "Can U Just".

"FUCK!" I realise I said this a bit too loud.

Wife has issued me with another directive. "Can U Just pick up some cheese X."

Now, with cheese and cat litter in hand, I make it to the self-serve tills. I spot our friend "blue legs" stood at his till. His till has come to a halt due to a scanning issue, and as help approaches, his face slowly turns the same colour as the red light flashing on his till to indicate a problem.

I turn and realise why. His carefully orchestrated condom purchase has not registered on his scanner and requires a full-blown storewide speaker price check announcement by the disgusted middle-aged woman shop worker, who glares at him over her spectacles as she puts the microphone to her lips.

"PRICE CHECK REQUIRED, PRICE CHECK REQUIRED. THREE PACK OF RIBBED TROJAN WARRIORS, THAT'S THREE PACK OF RIBBED TROJAN WARRIORS, THANK YOU. FOR THE MAN IN SHORTS AT TILL SIX"

He made a break for it, and ran out quicker than I have seen anyone run before. At least he was wearing shorts. I could visibly see the blood return to his legs as his sprint gathered pace.

My "Can U Just" trip had come to an end, until next time that is (probably tomorrow). As I make my way to the car, passing the beggar and feeling jealous that he was in his comfy clothes, the trolley guy taps me on the shoulder and points to our house.

Wife is stood there in the window waving, "Can U Just get some bread!"

I spin on my heels and with a huge sigh, I head back in.

# "New year, New me"

As another year dawns I realise the same things I realise every year, I am a year older, an inch wider (the disappearance of my genitalia behind my gut is testament to this), I am a lot poorer, and my tolerance and patience to everyone and everything is that little bit lower (aren't I a ray of sunshine).

Then I remember that these are the least of my worries as at the dawn of every January, Wife will announce the details of our (as I have simply no choice) annual "New Year, New me" lifestyle change.

As I have mentioned in previous tales, Wife has this uncanny ability to pretty much forget the past (I wish I could). Case in point, EVERY January she proclaims to the world that we are turning over a new leaf and we are going to stick to whatever new fad she has decided we are pursuing.

Now at this point, I hear you say, "Just say no." Like to heroin, or to receiving a strap on, or getting into a stranger's car when he offers you a sweet (candy if you are Yankish). But, this is Wife, and as years of marriage has taught me, resistance is not an option.

Now the January leaf turn could be anything, and as I sit here recounting these annual traumas, one thing has remained constant over the years, we haven't reached February still practicing our new ways ONCE!

Now to any other species (basically any other than wives), the part of the brain that controls learning would say, "Hang on, this never fucking works." But, like a glitch in the Matrix, Wife resets at Midnight on the 31st of December, and the January of failure has been wiped from the memory bank, and we march blindly into the new year, and a new January, destined for much of the same.

I feel the need at this point to say that I am all for the pursuit of new horizons, learning new things and bettering myself. And as I sit here, I can think of many things I would have definitely continued on into February if Wife had merely suggested them. Such as, relentless practice of Tantric Sex, joining a Gin club and exploring the world of recreational drugs. Or, better still, a combination of all three.

But, there is an ingredient included in all of my alternatives that Wife overlooks every year, FUN! The only guarantee every January (other than finding Christmas tree pine needles in underwear until May) is that whatever "New year, New Me" is this year, it will be as much fun as being water boarded and having my fingernails removed by the CIA.

So, that brings me full circle to this year. As New Year's Day dawns, I brace myself to find out what the "New Year, New Me" is going to be this year.

"Happy New Year!" Wife exclaims as I enter the kitchen in pursuit of a cup of the second-best Colombian product that could get me through the day.

I am severely hungover, I drank so much on New Year's Eve that according to the governments' alcohol unit intake guidance, I am not due my next drink until Halloween.

"Guess what today is?" Wife asks. I know I am in trouble due to the manic grin.

"Tuesday?" I manage to mutter in response while sipping my coffee.

"Well yes, it is. But, more importantly it is the first day of the rest of our lives!" Wife proclaims.

On hearing this, I vomit ever so slightly into my mouth.

"Meaning what?" As if I don't already know.

"Well, we are going to turn over a new leaf, and start as we mean to go on." She is still smiling.

As I scan the kitchen surveying the seemingly endless amount of empty wine and beer bottles from the night before, I try to establish which one I could reach the easiest to apply to Wife's head.

"Well, what is it this year? Yoga? Dry January (over my dead body)? Learn Japanese? Join the Gym (again)? Cycling? Sponsor a Mountain Gorilla? Or, all of the above?" I fear my sarcasm has jeopardised my safety.

"Now don't be like that, it is for your own good," Wife says while waiting to drop the bomb.

Here it comes… "This year we are going VEGAN!" She is actually smiling.

I feel numb, and at that moment my desire for bacon becomes uncontrollable.

"Not Vegan! No fucking way!" I don't know why I am protesting, Wife is already furiously scribbling on her vegan meal planner, and has already meticulously planned our meals for the next seven days.

"But I need meat, I am…" My protest ends there as I realise Wife has left the room to prepare for our impending vegan food shop.

Now, I want to make something very clear, I do not have anything against veganism, if it makes you happy, healthy and makes you feel good, great, but it is NOT for me.

I don't mind anyone being vegan or vegetarian, just don't force it on me (like Wife is).

I recall a bunch of vegans (extremists, granted) blocking the meat section in a supermarket while holding banners and stopping people buying meat.

It is the equivalent of me blocking the vegetable aisle preventing people indiscriminately murdering carrots, and separating shallots from their parents.

Sorry I digress.

Upon arrival at the supermarket, trolley (cart, if you are Americanese) in hand, we embark on our first plant-based shop.

The first forty-five minutes consisted of purchasing copious amounts of fruit, vegetables, soy milk and other things I can't pronounce.

As wife reaches for her enormous shopping list, she highlights the next thing we "need", oh joy.

"Right, we need to get plenty of legumes." Wife declares.

What the fuck are legumes? I thought he played for Real Madrid.

"You Know!" (I Don't)

"Chickpeas, lentils, you know," Wife barks.

After obtaining our "legumes", we approach the

"plant-based" frozen section. Now here we purchase our Nut Wellington, which resembles a vacated wasp's nest.

After what seems like days, we depart the supermarket with our vegan menu packed with enough fibre to move the bowels of a particularly "backed up" T-Rex.

En route home, we pass the familiar glow of the meat palace with the golden arches, observing the enormous queue of cars wrapped round the building waiting for their meaty treats.

"We are leaving all that unhealthy junk behind us now." Wife proclaims.

Wife is right. As I notice the golden arches getting ever smaller in my rear view mirror, I recall Wife on many occasions craving a Big Mac, fries, milkshake and apple pie so badly, she would spit and swear so much, she resembled someone who needed a priest to perform an exorcism upon her.

Once we returned home and unpacked our vegan shop, our kitchen resembled a greenhouse.

That evening we sat down for our first vegan dinner, and we both tucked into our Wasp Nest Wellington. To say it was awful was an understatement, it tasted like something you would force feed someone to obtain a confession.

"That was nice, wasn't it?" Wife remarked.

I managed to look at Wife's face briefly to see her mouth twitching ever so slightly. This is a woman on the edge.

I wanted to say it was the worst thing ever to enter my body, but my mouth said, "Yes, lovely."

In the moments after "dinner", I had to excuse myself. My first day of veganism had brought on relentless stomach cramps that told me I had to answer the call of nature.

The bathroom violence that ensued was something I would never forget, and by the end I swear I saw a tear run down the side of the toilet bowl. If it could talk, it would have begged for death.

After two days of vegan hell, and becoming weaker by the second, at around nine p.m. on day three of "New Year, New Me", things started to go downhill fast.

Wife had stopped talking and was gripping the arm of the sofa so tight, I was worried she may lose her arm due to lack of circulation.

If I had made eye contact with her, I would have certainly been killed. The lack of meat was taking its toll, and I was worried Wife was looking for any excuse to crush me.

Now at this point, I want to share some advice with all the husbands out there. There are times you have to throw yourself under the bus for the greater good. Let me elaborate...

This was due to the vegan nightmare we are going through, but more importantly due to wife not wanting to admit "New Year, New Me" was again, a disaster.

Now my advice is if (in my case) you want to see the return of steak night, then you have to do the noble thing and take the blame.

The only route out of this is for me to buckle first, and then Wife has someone to blame for the next eleven months and three weeks.

You see, husbands, Wife will save face in front of everyone because when asked by our friends, "How is the veganism going?"

Guess what? Wife can say, "Husband gave up." Then normality can resume.

Let me demonstrate.

I summon the strength to talk.

"Are you hungry?" I mutter to wife. Upon hearing those words her top lip starts to quiver, and I can see her gritted teeth. It is reminiscent of Clint Eastwood just before he shoots someone.

"What the fuck do you think? What a stupid fucking question!" she snarls.

I think it is safe to say she is hungry.

"Right, come on, get in the car," I say bravely.

After prying Wife's claws from the sofa, we embark on our journey of capitulation, and arrive at the golden arches within minutes.

The inevitable words come as we sit in the car park, under the glow of the golden arches, and Wife lifts the lid of the box of her Big Mac.

"This is your fault," Wife says.

But behind those words she is really saying thank you, and I can hear that loud and clear. The blame has been put at my door, and I am more than willing to accept it.

While the last slurp of Wife's milkshake disappears, I feel a sharp pain in a very delicate area, and as I pull the Christmas tree pine needle from my underwear, I realise that February is still weeks away. Some things never change.

# Take Away Tears

Picture the scene, it's been a long hard week at work, and it's home time on Friday. A whole evening of wearing my comfy clothes (predominantly garments made of elastic, so they don't remind me of how much I have let myself go) and drinking so much that by ten p.m. Wife will have to communicate with me by sign language.

The ecstasy on my face is abundant, as I pull over and skip into the shop for the evening's alcohol supplies.

I am feeling sophisticated, so I purchase a moderately priced bottle of Chianti (anything over £4.99 is pushing the boat out) and six cans of cider (90s child), and I grab Wife a bottle her favourite cocktail, Espresso Martini.

Espresso Martini is a disgusting beverage. My theory is that it was invented on a works do, and at the end of the night, Alan from Accounts in a critically drunken state, and in his desperation to get laid, decided he would pour Susan's (from HR) vodka & Michelle's (from Marketing) Tia Maria into his after dinner coffee in a vain attempt to convince both ladies that he was the type of man that lived on the edge and didn't give a fuck.

However, it didn't work. Susan and Michelle never spoke to Alan ever again, because after drinking this vile mixture, Alan immediately expressed himself all over Susan and Michelle, showering them in the world's first Espresso Martini.

Well, that's my theory anyway, and it is more entertaining than the probable truth. I can't believe it was ever created on purpose and that after the first sip, its creator said, "Oooo that's nice."

But Wife loves the stuff.

After giving the homeless man outside the shop some change, and momentarily fearing he would make a grab for my cider, I make my way home, safe in the knowledge I have all the lubrication (not that kind of lubrication) I need for a great evening.

I literally bounce through the door and present wife with her vile mixture.

"Oooo Espresso Martini, lovely!" Wife squeals, as she reached for her cocktail glass.

Right, first job, comfy clothes. After stripping off my work clothes, I decide what to put on. I go for an eclectic outfit of Sesame Street pyjama bottoms, and a jumper I bought when dinosaurs roamed the earth.

I look in the mirror, and for a split second I felt the inclination to give my reflection some loose change, and make sure I had a grip on my wallet.

As I make my way to the kitchen to start my alcohol fuelled evening, Wife is at the kitchen table sipping her Espresso Martini.

"Shall we get a takeaway?" she asks.

Now normally upon hearing such a question, I would instantly be transported on a culinary journey in my mind, deciding what style of food will grace my palette this evening.

But, I am currently stood in the kitchen dressed like a crack addict who would gladly satisfy any sexual perversion for a bump.

"Are you fucking kidding me?" I say while glaring at Wife.

"You LOVE take-out food!" She is right, I do.

"Yes, but you watched me walk in, go upstairs, get changed, and now you want me to not have a drink and go out to pick up a takeaway? Look at me, if I go out like this the fucking Salvation Army will corner me and cover me in blankets!"

"Don't be silly, you look fine. No one will see you," Wife states.

Now, what Wife really means here is that she will not see any one seeing me, as she won't be leaving the house. Surprise, surprise.

"No one will see me? I have pictures of Big Bird and Elmo all over my legs. That's why the fucking SAS don't wear Sesame Street pyjamas on covert missions, because they'd be gunned down in seconds."

I think I have made my point.

"Get it delivered then," Wife suggests.

Now, a reasonable suggestion I hear you say. However, there is one problem. It is Friday, and that means by the time my pizza gets delivered, mankind will be no more, mother nature will have reclaimed the earth, and my skeleton (in Sesame Street pyjama bottoms) will be being used as a polar bear's scratching post.

It is already seven thirty p.m. at this point, so I call it.

"OK, delivery it is then," I proclaim, as I will be damned if I am removing my comfy clothes to pick up the food.

Then, I utter the question every man dreads to ask

their wife when his hunger depends on it.

"What are you having?" I ask. I fall silent, as Wife reaches for the menu that I could read to you from memory in four different languages.

Wife grabs and opens the menu. She falls silent for what seems like an eternity.

As I sit there, sipping my second can of cider watching Wife's brain literally melt while she tries to make a decision, my mind begins to wonder whether my lawyer could argue that chronic hunger was to blame for my actions.

Then, she draws breath…

"What are you having?"

Now, at this point, I am going to momentarily step away from my account to talk to all my fellow husbands who no doubt suffer this response time after time.

The first thing to say to you all, is that you are not alone. The "what are you having?" question seems to be a universal female response to any menu-based decision in a restaurant, bar, or anywhere that involves a choice.

However, the odd thing here is that whatever you are having (which you undoubtedly decided an hour ago) has no bearing on Wife's decision.

But fellow husbands, please be mindful of a term I have coined when it comes to female menu decisions. It is called "Guilt Spreading" and the female is a cunning master in this practice.

Let me explain…

The REAL reason Wife wants to know, "What are you having?" is not to see if she wants to order the same, but to engage in "Guilt Spreading". With this seemingly innocent question, she is establishing if you are ordering something she wants to steal from you.

The guilt of ordering a mixed grill special kebab, with a calorific content the same as the blubber from a blue whale, would be too much for her to handle.

So, because you are ordering it, NO GUILT! It is like the calories don't count because she is stealing it from you.

So next time she orders her grilled chicken kebab, remember your donner meat and fries mountain that you ordered will not be safe.

The final angle here before I resume my account, is the classic, "I will have a few of yours". This refers to the side dish attack.

It goes like this, "Are you ordering fries?" Wife enquires.

"Yes, definitely. Are you?" I ask

"Me? No, I will just have a few of yours."

There you have it, your fries are history. But because Wife hasn't ordered them, it is like they never existed.

So, when Wife can't work out why she has only lost two ounces at Slimming World this week, and you have lost three pounds without trying, it is because you have fallen victim to "Guilt Spreading".

Now back to my account…

"It doesn't matter what I am having, you choose your own."

"I just want to know," Wife asks.

"OK, I am having a mixed grill kebab," I proclaim. This kebab is so large that in some countries if you were stopped and searched while in possession of this kebab, you could arrested on deadly weapons charges.

"I will have a grilled chicken kebab," Wife has decided.

What a shock, I could have predicted this an hour ago.

"Right, I am ordering it," I say as I finish my second cider and reach for the phone.

"Hang on. Are you having fries?" Wife enquires.

"Yes, do you want some?" This is so predictable.

"Oh no, I'll have a few of yours." Shocker.

It is now eight fifteen p.m.

So, now we reach the next hurdle. I need to phone my order through. With hunger now gnawing away at me, I make the call.

I don't know what it is about calling the kebab house, situated two miles away. In 1969 US President, Richard Nixon Spoke to the astronauts live on the surface of the moon, on a clear uninterrupted line.

Literally, Neil Armstrong could've ordered any kebab he wanted, and they would not have forgotten the stuffed crust on Buzz Aldrin's Pizza.

As I ring my order through, Ahmet answers the phone just two miles away, and it sounds like he is speaking from the bottom of the Atlantic.

I can barely hear him screaming down the phone demanding my order, with the clattering of pans and skewers in the background, while forty men hurl expletives in Turkish at each other.

I eventually manage to get my order across to him, after my fourth attempt. I could have walked there and wrote on his hand in Biro in less time.

"How long will it be?" I ask, bracing myself for his response.

"One hour," he barked – at least that is what I think he said.

Now, this is a predictable response from Ahmet. It is ALWAYS one hour.

If Ahmet had created heaven and earth, he would have done it in an hour.

If Ahmet had flown solo round the world, he would have done it in an hour.

If Ahmet was asked by the Pharaoh's to build the great Pyramid at Giza, it would've taken him an hour.

And, just to hammer the point home, Ahmet ran the London marathon last year in an hour.

So, during our one hour wait, I decide to drink heavily while Wife retreats to the living room to watch a mind-numbing soap opera, while she looks forward to eating my fries.

Now, our house is quite tucked away, and not very well lit. Due to this, I feel the need to keep an eye out for the delivery guy (Ahmet's Brother Berat) who can drive anywhere on the surface of the earth in one hour.

So, after polishing off cider number four, my patience is getting thin. I decide to leave wife to her soaps and wait on the porch for Berat to arrive.

I tuck into cider number five while I await Berat outside, so I can guide him in like an air traffic controller.

The one-hour delivery time came and went, and by this time, I was well on my way to being sensationally pissed.

I decide to wander to the end of the road to see if I

can spot Berat driving round in circles, looking for our house that he has been to countless times.

But, alas, no Berat in sight.

I am now drunk, ravenous and stood on the street.

Now from here my account does get a bit hazy.

One thing I do recall is Wife shouting at me from the doorstep and asking, "Is the food here yet?"

"Yes, I have eaten mine on the street, and fed yours to next doors dog"

"Really?" Wife asks.

"No, not really dear, it's called wit," is my rather slurred response.

I recall Wife slamming the door and returning to her shite on TV.

As I return my focus to the street in wait for Berat, I take the first swig of Chianti from my moderately priced purchase, and then I see a figure approach.

My heart leapt in excitement (or I was having a heart attack, one of the two) could it be? Is Berat finally here? I focus on the figure emerging from the darkness into the glow of one of the street lamps, I realise it isn't Berat.

It is a man dressed in equally impressive comfy clothes.

"Evening," I say cautiously to the stranger.

Men often say "Evening" to strangers in the dark when what they actually mean is, "Who the fuck are you?"

The stranger replies with an equally unimpressive, "Evening."

As we lock eyes and decide what to say next to each other, the smell of stale piss and body odour fill the air around me.

I think to myself, "Am I that pissed? Have I lost my bladder in front of a complete stranger?"

No, my Sesame Street pyjamas are dry, my dignity remains intact for now.

Before I could utter another word to break the ice with my new "friend", I spot a van approaching at speed.

At last! It must be Berat with hot kebabs! I take a celebratory sip of Chianti and offer my new comfy clothed friend a slurp.

As the van comes to a halt, the door flings open, and I can almost taste the donner meat, when a female voice says…

"You poor souls." That is not Berat, it is the fucking Salvation Army.

The interior lights of the van illuminate the face of my new drinking buddy for the first time, it is the homeless guy from outside the shop I encountered earlier.

I am in a state of shock, as the Salvation Army throw blankets over our shoulders, coax my chianti from my hand and usher us into their van.

"You're not Berat, where's my kebab?" I ask the Salvation Army lady.

She turns to her colleague driving the van with concern and mutters to him.

"He's delirious," she whispers.

I realise we have been kidnapped, and I am on route the nearest homeless shelter.

"Now listen, you have this all wrong. I live here, take me back, my wife will be worried sick." But she is not listening.

Actually, Wife won't be worried sick, I doubt she will even notice that I have been kidnapped from the street.

At some point of the journey I realise I am sipping hot soup from a polystyrene cup (not bad actually) that the Salvation Army lady had given to me. I am grateful as it is the first nourishment I have had all evening.

On arrival at the shelter, I had sobered up enough to explain to my Salvation Army kidnappers that this was all a misunderstanding, and I was not a homeless person.

I offered my captors the opportunity to sniff me, as I thought my distinct lack of piss smell would be enough to convince them, even though the place was full of people in their "comfy clothes" dressed just like me.

After much negotiation, I was released into the night. I bid farewell to my new vagrant friend (never did get his name) and after tearing my remaining half bottle of Chianti from his secret pocket in his pissed stained coat, I head home.

Upon reaching the end of my street, my attention turns back to my take away. I reach my house just as Berat is pulling up outside in his van.

As I entered the house, Wife was still glued to the TV.

"Is that you? Is the food here?" she shouts from the living room.

"Yes, it is me, and yes the food is here," I reply.

I never did tell Wife what happened that night, and as we sit and eat, I wonder if I had passed out outside, and the whole thing was just some sort of drunken nightmare.

A few days later, I spot the homeless guy outside the shop again, so I give him some change again, and I walk on.

I remember thinking as I walked away that it must have been a dream, and I must have blacked out waiting for Berat to eventually turn up with my horrendously late takeaway.

Then, without warning I turn to see the homeless guy singing the theme song to "Sesame Street" at the top of his voice, while waving at me.

# "Baby Oil Blues"

It was inevitable I suppose that I would reach this subject at some point. Yeah, you got it. Being told to stay home by Boris (Johnson that is, the British prime minister in case you are Americanish, or you have been living underground the past year).

As I write this, I am a recluse with an enormous beard, and an alcohol problem so big that it is quite the norm to be blind drunk by the time "Loose Women" starts on ITV.

However, it didn't start this way. When we were initially all told to "Stay Home" by Boris, I thought, "Right, I am going use this time to reconnect with my family, learn new life skills, read all the books I have been meaning to read, maybe learn a new language."

But no, three weeks in I look like an alcoholic "Hagrid" from Harry Potter, in a dressing gown and googly eyed dinosaur slippers.

I spend most of my mornings eating cake, and watching repeat episodes of "Murder, she wrote". After watching all two hundred and sixty-four episodes (that's accurate, look it up) I have developed a very disturbing and strange attraction to "Jessica Fletcher" (Angela Lansbury) which, is even more disturbing than my beard.

I haven't fantasised about her yet, but in these strange times, I wouldn't rule out imagining Jessica Fletcher removing my googly dinosaur slippers with her teeth, and running her wrinkly detective fingers through my beard, freeing up pieces of trapped Genoa cake and feeding them to me.

I haven't thought about this, honestly.

Speaking of cake, it has now got that bad that when Wife is not around, I will hold a slab of Genoa cake like you would hold a Snickers Bar, and eat the lot before we find out from "Jessica Fletcher" who the killer is.

There was a point where I actually forgot Wife and I had kids, as they had retreated to their rooms about ten days ago, and unless we have a power cut (therefore, no Xbox), the next time I see them they will also have full beards.

Now seeing this a confessional account, I want to document my shame. Every morning, I have to do the "walk of shame" in my dinosaur slippers, of course, to the recycling bin.

A mundane, shameless task I hear you say, and in any other time in history you would be right, but during this enforced house arrest, the trip to the recycling bin is a humiliation.

This is due to the disposal of last night's empties, which there are many, and when I say many, I mean many.

Now there are two choices here with the walk of shame.

### Option 1 "Blitzkreig"

Go out very early to dispose of your shame, and do a quick raid. Dispose of everything as quickly as possible.

Although you risk the noise of crashing glass waking

a neighbour, and them seeing you through the curtains, witnessing how much of a problem you have while shaking their head at you (been there, done that).

However, if you are quick enough, by the time they hear the almighty crash you have sprinted into the house. While your neighbour is left to wonder who is to blame.

A word of advice, I would practice running in your googly eyed slippers before undertaking this method for the first time. I speak from experience, as a successful empties drop was ruined during my first sprint.

My left slipper lost an eye, and received a rather large dose of dog shit due to my inexperience.

### **Option 2 "Hide in plain sight"**

This is the covert method, using stealth to creep out in plain sight during the day. This is a high-risk strategy as the method involved here requires a steady hand. Now, a steady hand can be a problem, as the amount I am drinking at the moment, means my hands shake like windmills. Now once at the bin, you carefully PLACE each empty delicately in the bin without attracting attention.

There is no margin for error here, as one false move and the crashing glass means you are laid bare for the whole street to see.

Now my afternoons are consumed by trying to decide when is the earliest time I can start drinking without prompting Wife to organise an "intervention".

The acceptable time at the moment is circa three p.m. Luckily the weather is really good at the moment, so I can get away with three p.m. if I sit in the garden.

Weird, isn't it? If I sit in the garden with a drink,

looking at flowers in the sunshine at three p.m., it's fine with Wife. But, sat on the couch drinking at three p.m., eating cake and watching "Gavin & Stacey" would mean a death sentence.

So, onto my account. In all honesty, I think this all happened in one day, but I can't be sure as I have been drunk or hung over since March. But, I will try and piece it together.

"Rise & Shine!" Wife squeals as she throws open the bedroom curtains.

The sun beamed down on me from the window so brightly that for a moment I thought I was going to need a golden retriever to guide me for the rest of my life.

As I slowly regain my sight, and I see Wife's silhouette come into view, and in that instant, I would have gladly pushed wife from said window, but I remember we live in a three storey, and the chances of survival were small.

Only when she moves from the window, I remember the kids' trampoline was below, and would have reduced the odds of death to an acceptable level.

"Come on, get up lazy bones." She is smiling way too much.

"Why? Where are we going?" I snap.

"We are going out for our essential shopping." She is still smiling way too much.

"Oh God." I attempt to roll over, but Wife has yanked and removed the duvet to expose my Sesame Street pyjama pants, and I realise that it was futile to resist.

"C'mon, chop, chop!" she cries.

I roll out of bed, and crawl to the bathroom. As I

stand in front of the mirror looking at what lockdown had done to me, I wondered if I would ever be the same again.

Don't get me wrong, I have always drank and ate well, too well. But as I look at my bearded reflection, I look like a very hungover Yeti in Sesame Street Pyjamas.

After showering, admiring my beard for a while and squeezing myself into "real clothes" (when I say "real clothes", I mean clothes that don't have cartoon characters on them or elasticated waists) that fit me a few weeks ago, and I take one last look in the mirror before heading downstairs.

I notice in the mirror that my grey skinny jeans are so tight that it looks like my naked legs have just been sprayed in grey primer.

As ridiculous as I look, I take the decision to leave them on and not change, as I fear that the effort required to remove them may result in me having a cardiac arrest.

To complete the look, I go for the biggest t-shirt I own, as it is the only garment big enough to cover the vast muffin top I had developed.

Now, looking like a 1970s darts player (with an equally large drink problem), I manage to navigate the stairs somehow, almost without bending my knees due to my jeans cutting of my circulation.

"Are you OK?" Wife asks. I think she noticed my feet turning purple.

"Not really, I think I may have put on a couple of pounds." At this point if I had breathed out, the top button on my jeans would've penetrated the patio window and killed next doors cat from two hundred yards.

At this point Wife could see the shame on my face,

and out of sympathy and a moment of tenderness (or not wanting to be seen in public with a fat, grey-legged bearded man, wearing a ships sail for a T-Shirt), she says...

"You stay here if you want, I'll go," Wife says.

I must admit, the thought of joining the back the socially distanced, mask-wearing queue of sandal and sock wearing OAPs, mobile phone staring under thirties, and sun burnt forty something's from baking in the sun, filled me with dread.

I couldn't believe my luck. In the excitement, I very nearly breathed out too hard, which would've resulted in me being in court trying to explain how my top button ended up in embedded in Wife's skull.

"Right, I am off then, why don't you get some exercise while I am gone? Get on the exercise bike."

As I am nodding in agreement, all I can think of is what time Murder, She Wrote starts, and thinking what Jessica Fletcher (the wrinkly minx) will be wearing in today's episode.

As Wife leaves on the promise I will get active while she is out, my thoughts turn to the removal of my jeans.

This is not going to be easy. At one point I seriously consider cutting them off with scissors, like a paramedic tending to a road traffic accident victim. But, I actually like these jeans, so the struggle begins.

The indignity of this task meant I couldn't risk trying this downstairs. The risk of the neighbours spotting me writhing and squirming on the floor, pulling at my jeans could easily result in them calling 999 and reporting me for sex crimes, or at best, I could have an ambulance arrive expecting to find an epilepsy sufferer in skinny jeans.

I manage to crawl upstairs and begin to tug away (at my jeans that is). I start to sweat and feel the frustration building.

If you have ever watched David Attenborough's "Planet Earth" program, you may be familiar with the episode where an African Rock Python sheds its skin. It is almost an exact re-enactment of this natural wonder, as I begin to try and peel these fucking jeans from my body.

Now, I want you to imagine in your mind that you can hear David Attenborough's voice documenting my struggle...

Here we have one of nature's most remarkable rituals. This enormous bearded husband is attempting to remove his trousers after weeks of gorging on Genoa cake and 'Murder, she wrote'. His bloated frame has outgrown his trousers to such an extent that if he does not remove his trousers soon, he may die.

"He is exhausted. If he does not shed these trousers quickly, the fearsome predator known as the sharp-tongued ball buster will return home. She will first deafen him with her relentless battle cries, then remove his genitals for fun, and displaying them for all to see."

Panic begins to set in as I realise I may have to wear skinny jeans for the rest of my days. Then, just as I reach near exhaustion, I have an idea. Baby oil.

I drag myself to the bathroom to apply Wife's baby oil down the front of my jeans, in the hope the extra lubrication will free me from my denim prison.

I look like a real pervert now; I am lying on the

bathroom floor with my hands down the front of my trousers trying to rub vast quantities of baby oil to my skin. People have been jailed for less than this.

Things take a disturbing turn as in the throes of rubbing myself stupid, and making some progress on getting my jeans to my thighs, I notice a shadow appear against the bathroom wall.

To my horror, I am being glared at by the window cleaner. I freeze, the window cleaner freezes, and in that moment as we lock eyes, I know he hasn't witnessed anything like this in his entire life, let alone his career.

"All right," I say while looking up at the ajar window, lying on the floor soaked in baby oil.

"Yeah, all right?" the window cleaner replied. I have never seen anyone clean a window as quick in my entire life.

Finally, after what seemed like hours, my jeans are off. They look like they have been used in a rather disturbing porn movie, as I quickly put them in the washing machine. Although, I will have to wait for Wife to get home as I don't know how to turn it on.

I think I have definitely achieved my cardio for the day, so my attention turns to alcohol, Genoa cake and Murder, She Wrote.

After returning to my natural habitat (the couch) with my cake in hand, and Sesame Street pyjamas covering my still slightly oily legs, I turn my attention to the opening credits of Murder, She Wrote.

Just as Jessica is at her typewriter to see in this rather arousing episode, I can hear Wife outside returning with the shopping.

She should be inside by now I thought, so I wander to the window to see her chatting to the window cleaner! My heart nearly stops. As he is talking casually to Wife, he makes eye contact with me and winks at me with a wry smile.

I quickly return to the couch before Wife can see me, just as she walks in.

"I'm back," Wife announces.

"The window cleaner was outside; he gave me his bill," Wife says while handing the envelope to me.

"Oh, really? He was quiet, I didn't hear anything. What did he say?" I ask while opening the envelope.

"Oh, nothing really, he asked how you were though," Wife said casually.

"Did he? That is nice," I say as I scan the bill.

The bill has our monthly charge of £20 crossed out, replaced with a hastily written £40 in Biro, a winking smiley face and scrawled note saying, "Your secret is safe with me!"

"The robbing bastard!"

# Tinkering

My anonymity is very important here, as I may be targeted by husbands up and down the land for divulging too many truths in this chapter.

There are few places in this world where a husband can find solitude. Don't get me wrong, I love being around my dogs, cats, kids and wife (preferably in that order) but every husband needs to find some time for himself.

I guess every husband has his "my time" place, where he can reflect, contemplate, meditate, relax and view pornography to his heart's content.

Some husbands have a converted bedroom that has become an "office" at home, with a desk, office chair, laptop (an essential for Pornhub), a box of man size tissues (for his sinuses, yeah right), and stationary.

He will spend endless hours in solitude pretending to work in his "home office" while periodically remembering to shake his box of paperclips and print blanks sheets of paper so Wife downstairs can't hear the moans and groans from the latest "Fake Taxi" episode. (Apparently, "Fake Taxi" is a mocked up taxi that picks up porn stars, and then the "driver" has his way with them. I obviously had no idea what this was, and had to do lengthy sessions of "research" for the sake of my art.

Anyway, moving on...)

Other husbands have a "shed" that they retreat to so they can tinker (masturbate). Although, when Husband was building the "shed", Wife could never understand why Husband didn't buy a shed with a window, and why it needed a lock on the inside, and why Husband always needed to take the laptop with him to "tinker".

These peculiarities, such as the reason for the lock on the inside, were usually explained away by Husband as, "I don't want to be disturbed." (I bet he doesn't.)

As for the lack of a window, "It'll get too hot" would be a common excuse to give to Wife. The real reason being he doesn't want to be spotted by Gillian next door pulling himself sideways, while Gillian is doing her Pilates.

The reason for taking the laptop to the "shed" (dungeon of filth), he explained to Wife, was to "watch tutorial videos" of how to wood carve, or to learn the finer arts of joinery.

In reality, Husband will watch many "tutorial videos" which he will find exhausting, demanding and educational.

Also, Wife will not understand the need for a water dispenser in the Pleasure Palace—sorry, "Shed". But, after weeks of "education" in the shed, Husband will learn the true value of hydration.

There are some husbands who take up a "hobby" or a new "sport" in pursuit of his "my time". These activities can include taking up golf or fishing, and involve spending many hours perfecting their new passion.

Now, I have a theory here. Taking up golf or fishing

is usually a sign that Husband has not had an erection since Kate Bush was on Top of the Pops.

Now, to take Husband's mind off his "issues", Husband will take up golf in the vain attempt to display his dominance over his new "golf buddies" – to compensate for the fact that his phalis hasn't reached for the sky since Kate belted out "Wuthering Heights" in her flowy dress.

He will spend thousands on the latest golf equipment, to show off, and to get ahead of his equally flaccid "golf buddies" and to become the alpha male in his new pride.

I also have a theory regarding golf attire. Husbands will happily dress in ridiculously loud check trousers, white golf shoes and lemon yellow golf shirts. This to me is a cry for help, and a subliminal admission they have not had sex since Tiger Woods was four years old.

I also think that the time it takes to complete a round of golf (especially if you are as shit as Husband) plays a big part here.

This means Husband can spend even more time out of the home and away from the constant reminder that some his sperm have developed arthritis, and require a Zimmer frame.

Even after a seven-hour round of golf, rather than going home to Wife to work on his "putting" with her, he'd rather spend another four hours in the clubhouse drinking and talking absolute bullshit about how good he was today "out there" and how he dominated the holes.

In truth, Husband has not dominated a hole since the Millennium, when Wife was dressed in a horse bridle, and Husband nearly choked on a ball gag while "breaking her in".

Now fishing is a whole other ball game. Husband would literally prefer to sit on an embankment all night in the pissing rain, freezing his inactive balls off, gripping his ten foot pole, than be at home in bed with Wife.

Now, some husbands just need some genuine "me time", and this leads me to my place, where I can have some time to myself without being disturbed, or at least that's the idea.

It's a bitterly cold evening when Wife and I return from hours of retail torment that she has subjected me to.

As I fall through the door, weighed down with the countless shopping bags we have accumulated through the day, I drop them unceremoniously on the kitchen floor, before my already blue finger tips fall off.

As Wife excitedly begins to unpack the one billion items I have paid for (sorry, 'we' have paid for) I begin to worry that my extremities will begin to fall off if I don't warm up soon.

Also, for the past six hours I have been Wife's shopping partner, which is the equivalent of being dragged by my scrotum through the streets and having deafening screeching being pumped into my ear canals.

But, I made it home. I don't think Wife is listening to me when I declare, "I am going for a bath!"

Wife is too busy unpacking all the items we bought that we don't need.

So, I can reveal the bath is "My Place" where I can allow my ears and extremities recover from a day in retails hell.

"I said, I am going for a bath!" I want to make sure

Wife understands that it means DO NOT DISTURB.

"I heard you," she cries, as if I should know she heard me even though she never paused tearing the bags open for a second.

I leave wife to her bag tearing, and head upstairs to my sanctuary. Not before nearly dying on the stairs due to my steamed-up glasses.

At last! I close the bathroom door and shut out the world for hopefully at least an hour or so. Now I want to add at this point that I have no intention of "tinkering" or catching up with any "tutorial videos" (see Shed Life above). My intentions are wholesome (for today).

My sole purpose today is to prevent my toes being buried in the back garden by the dog after they succumb to frostbite.

I turn on the taps and pour enough bubble bath in the water to have my own Ibiza foam party. I then carefully begin to remove my clothes, trying not to cause any of my fingers or toes to fall off.

So, suitably naked, I am ready to slide into the bubble abyss and drift away. Just before I do take the plunge, I catch a glimpse of my naked body in the mirror, and for a split second I thought my penis had been removed with my underwear.

I looked like Buffalo Bill from "Silence of the Lambs" when he tucked his penis between his legs.

I realise (thankfully) that my penis had not fallen off, but it had deserted me. I am so cold that the area where my penis should be, now resembles a Walnut Whip (google it).

Evidently, my penis was so cold that he thought,

"fuck this, I'm off" and retreated to a warmer climate –
namely inside my body.

It looked like puberty had reversed itself.

To rectify this situation and to lure my penis back into
the light, I carefully step into the bubble mountain that
had developed in the tub.

To my horror the water is so hot, that I scream
"Fuck!" so loudly that it is enough to attract Wife to the
bathroom door.

"You OK?" she asks from the other side of the door.

Sarcasm gets the better of me. "Oh yeah, I often
scream fuck at the top of my lungs to express my
contentment."

"OK, no need for sarcasm," Wife barks back.

I attempt to explain.

"Sorry, I don't have much time. If I don't persuade my
penis to return soon, he may decide that he prefers the
warmth of living behind my testicles."

"You filthy animal, are you tinkering in there?" Wife
enquires.

Even if I was "tinkering", am I really likely to scream
at the top of my lungs "fuck" while secretly pleasuring
myself?

"No, I am not!" I shout.

With that I hear Wife's footsteps retreating
downstairs.

At this point I apply plenty of cold water to my bath
to bring the temperature under volcanic levels.

My scalded leg looks so red it resembles a Maine
American lobster ready to have a wedge of lemon
squeezed over it.

Naked, burned, and lacking a penis, I attempt bath entry number two.

It's perfect! I slide in there like Casanova's tongue sliding into a love conquest.

As I settle in my watery heaven, I feel my penis being tempted to return to me. Slowly but surely, he emerges from his sanctuary. I also narrowly avoid choking to death on bubbles, but after a coughing fit, all is well.

Can you imagine if I had choked in the bath? Wife would have to explain why her husband was found dead in the bath with the penis of a ten-year-old, one lobster red leg and lungs filled with bubble bath.

In her trial, the prosecution would try and convince the jury and convict her on the basis of a sex game gone wrong (chance would be a fine thing).

I almost feel like a man again, and as I drift into near state of total relaxation... There is a knock.

"What is it? I shriek.

"Can I come in?" Wife enquires.

I want to tell her to fuck off, but as a husband you have to play the long game.

"Ok, what is it?" Before I finish my sentence, the door opens.

"I want your opinion, how do I look?" Wife steps into the bathroom to interrupt my vibe, and through the steam she steps (like in "Stars in their Eyes" but thank Jesus she does not try to sing) and I focus on her.

Wife is stood their wearing a new top (£50) which resembles a torn pillow case with semen stains on it.

"What do you think?" Wife awaits my response.

Now, a word of advice husbands, Wife does NOT

want to know what you think or your opinion.

In the spirit of survival, she wants to hear you say, "Wow you look amazing!"

So, I respond...

"Wow, you look amazing!" I proclaim, while smiling broadly.

"Aw, you think so?" Wife asks.

"Yes, you look amazing. Now can you close the door, you are letting out all the heat."

"Oh, OK." And with that, I am once again alone with my newly returned penis.

I catch a glimpse of me in the mirror now that Wife has let all the steam out, and the bubbles in the bath are so deep that it looks like my severed head is sat on a cloud of bubbles.

I am in paradise now my body has thawed. There is however a missing ingredient, alcohol.

I scream for Wife, and eventually out of concern, rather than anything else, she returns.

"Can you grab a glass of wine for me?" I plead.

"You do look great by the way," I add, softening the ground – take heed husbands.

"OK," she crumbles.

Boom, control through compliments. It never fails (you can have that one).

"Here you are." Wife presents me with a bottle of Malbec and a glass.

"Thank you, love you," I say lovingly as Wife retreats back downstairs.

I have to try really hard not to laugh at her, as she looks like a walking cum-stained pillowcase in her new top. I manage to keep a straight face long enough for the door to close.

I pour my wine and sip away. Warm, content and with penis again.

Now things get hazy from here, but I will attempt to document the remaining part of my account to the best of my recollection.

I do recall after many hot water top ups, and glasses of wine, I hear Wife at the door once more.

"I am going to bed in a minute, are you OK?" she asks with concern.

"Yes, I am absolutely fine. You go to bed, I will come to bed in a little while."

I think Wife is just happy I have not drowned, as I hear her retreat to the bedroom.

The next thing I do remember is waking with a jolt and a splash, with a mouthful of cold water. I had demolished my wine (all of it) and nodded off in the bath.

To my horror upon waking, I had realised that I had repeatedly vomited in the bath, turning the now cold water in to a red wine stained pool with floating fragments of my lunch (Nando's).

In the panic, I emptied the cold, red vomit-laden bath water and force as much of my fragmented lunch down the plug hole as I possibly can.

Once emptied, I remove my naked frame from the bath, and manage to apply my underwear without falling due to my drunken state.

I do remember navigating my path to the bedroom in the dark, with as much care and attention as could be applied considering I am blind drunk.

I make it into bed without waking Wife, and fall into a deep, drunken sleep.

The next morning...

"What the fuck!" Wife shrieks.

I open my very hung over eyes to see Wife stood next to the bed, obviously fuming.

"What is it? Please don't shout, my head is pounding," I plead.

"Look at you!" she cries

"What is it?" I peel myself out of bed and look in the bedroom mirror.

The sight I am faced with in the mirror will stay with me for the rest of my life. Due to vomit-laden red wine bath water, my entire body was stained red from my chin downwards.

I looked like a six foot jelly baby.

To Wife's horror, her new sheets from yesterday's shopping trip that I had just slept on had the outline of my wine-stained body permanently imprinted on.

"Look at this!" she wailed, while holding up the newly stained (expensive) sheet.

It looked like Elmo had died on it.

To say I wasn't popular, was an understatement to end all understatements.

Needless to say, I had to replace the sheets. I also had to cover my entire body for the next two weeks, and Wife had to apply make up to my neck so I could go to work.

On the plus side, my penis had returned, albeit stained red. Also, I have taken many trouble-free baths since this episode, and if there is one lesson I have learned, DO NOT drink and bathe.

# "Paradise Lost"

It was Phil Collins who famously penned the song "Another Day in Paradise" in 1989 for his album... But Seriously.

Now, before I begin this account, I firstly I want to make it very clear that I can't stand Phil Collins (his music anyway).

I don't know Phil (I am sure he is a top bloke, maybe) but he always reminded me of that creepy little "uncle" (but wasn't really your uncle) you remember from childhood that never married, drove a van with blacked out windows, had surgically clean hands and always smelled of bleach.

Now, you may be wondering why I am laying into one of the UK's foremost artists. Well, I can explain, I think.

Being a husband is a tough job at the best of times. It is the equivalent of walking a tightrope (tightrope = life's journey) on a unicycle (unicycle = what life throws at you), but instead of a safety net waiting below to save you, Wife is there with a twelve inch kitchen knife, staring at you and almost praying for you to lose your balance.

Now I am metaphorically speaking here (I hope), but I would rather face the liquid metal Terminator (the one that can replicate anyone and morph itself into any knife or stabbing weapon) from Terminator 2, than face wife armed with a twelve inch kitchen knife.

In fact, I have woken up in a sweat on more than one occasion, after dreaming Wife had morphed her arm into a sword and pinned me to the fridge through my open mouth, as my body twitches for the final time, all for asking if she had put the bins out.

A husband's responsibilities and duties are wide ranging, and I have listed my ten husband commandments below for you.

Now, if you are a husband reading this, you may read these ten lifesaving guidelines below, and think that'll never apply to you. I would have done the same ten years ago because I fought against the tide.

But, if you want to, A) survive B) have sex ever again or C) not have your scissor tattered clothes strewn all over the driveway, I suggest you take on board some (if not all) of the list of truths, duties and responsibilities set out below.

The Biblical Ten Commandments pale in to insignificance, compared to the list below. I will now deliver the following list to you, and although it may not be easy reading, it may just stop you from starving to death or having to ejaculate into a sock for the rest of time.

Here I decree the following ten truths:

1, Thou art always wrong.

2, Thou shalt roll out heavy laden bins on bin day for eternity.

3, Thou Shalt accept and attempt every DIY job Wife throws at you, regardless of size and complexity until judgement day. Then, on completion, thou must fall to ones knees so Wife can tell thee how utterly shit thou are at DIY.

4, Thou must never watch football in peace ever again.

5, Thou shalt heap praise on Wife's cooking regardless of one's true feelings. Even if it tastes like pig swill, thou must smile through gritted teeth.

6, If thou is asked by Wife, "Do I look fat in this?" Never tell the truth. God will forgive your lies, as he understands the Wrath that thou will suffer.

7, Thou shall never protest about having no socks in thy sock drawer. If thy does protest, thou will be forever directed to the carrier bag full of unpaired socks, and thy will suffer workplace ridicule forever more due to wearing one business sock and one Garfield sock.

8, Thou shalt always remain silent when Wife is driving. Even if Wife performs a one-hundred-and-six-point turn, abandons a parallel park because it's "too tight" (even though thou could park an oil tanker in the space) or if Wife indicates right but turns left, nearly killing an innocent. Thy must not make eye contact or make a noise, as Wife will pounce on thee and force thou to walk home further than when the Israelites were led out of Egypt by Moses.

9, Thou shalt never complain when thy shower is blocked by Wife's hairballs. Thou must pull Wife's hairballs from thy drain in silence, without complaint, while wondering why Wife isn't bald as there is more hair here than on a Turkish man's back. Any protest will result in thou having to pleasure one's self until lent.

10, Thou shalt never talk or make eye contact when Wife is experiencing her "time of the month". Twelve times a year the dark angel Lucifer takes Wife's place for five days, and roams the earth in Wife's form, wearing her dressing gown, contorting her face, clutching a pink hot water bottle and trying to rid the earth of Cadbury's Dairy Milk.

Now the tenth commandment leads me perfectly on to my account. The day started like any other, but it didn't take long for me to realise that for the next five days, the gates of hell had opened.

I awoke to an empty bed (Wife is up), and the sound of my alarm, like any other day. But, unlike most days, my smart speaker would wake me to the sound of a classic track by some rock legend hero of mine, but not today.

I thought I was experiencing some kind of nightmare when I opened my eyes and could hear a foul sound, the equivalent to having vomit poured in my ears.

As "Oh, think twice" sang from speaker, I knew that voice anywhere, it was Phil Collins. As he sang the next line "It's another day for you and me in Paradise", I was trying to remember if I had any razors in the bathroom, or if I should jump from the front window and risk the neighbours seeing my lifeless naked body on the driveway as they go to work. Or, alternatively, jumping from the back window and risk landing in next door's back garden and destroying their bird table.

After deciding that the risk of not dying was too great, and having to pay for next door's bird table (rear window option) or having to face all the other neighbours after seeing my naked body on the driveway (front window option) with compound fractures, I decide to live on for today.

So, to escape this turmoil, I leap from my bed and go downstairs to escape this audible buggery.

Unfortunately, as I enter the kitchen, I can hear the radio still playing the same song, but thankfully Mr Collins sings the last "You and me in paradise" and the track fades.

"Morning!" I state a little too happily, mainly due to the fact Phil Collins had stopped singing.

I spot Wife in her dressing gown making a cup of tea with her back to me. There is no response from Wife, so I try a little harder.

"Morning!" I said this a little too loud.

"I heard you the first time! Yes, it's morning! Good fucking morning!" The level of sarcasm and sass is disturbing.

Now, I know something isn't right. At this point, as an experienced husband, I trawl my memory banks while checking the date.

Have I forgotten something? In my mind I quickly think, anniversary? Birthday? Valentine's day? No, definitely not one of those.

Have I done or not done something? Was I drunk last night? No, have I said something? No, I am at a loss to understand this level of venom.

However, all becomes clear when Wife turns to me clutching her hot water bottle. I now know the reason for her hostility. It is Wife's time of the month. For the next five days Wife will be replaced by Beelzebub, and I will be punished for having a penis.

"It's my time of the month," Wife decrees, as she stands there staring into my soul, concocting ways to blame me for all of womankind menstruating.

I make my first mistake, I speak.

"Oh dear, are you feeling rotten?" I don't know what possessed me to speak. I might as well of just placed my scrotum on the kitchen table and handed wife the Courgetti spiralizer.

"Feeling rotten? No, I feel on top of the fucking world!" Wife barks while reaching in the kitchen drawer.

To my relief, she didn't reach for the Spiralizer, just a teaspoon.

"I suppose you want a cup of fucking tea, don't you?" she asks, while glaring at me. She is breathing through her nose now, and her nostrils are flaring violently. As much as I want a cup of tea, I like having a penis.

I simply don't know what to say as any reply could result in me being beaten, hogtied, and kept under the stairs for the foreseeable future.

I have to say something to Wife, as silence when being spoken to would be seen as an act of war.

"No, you sit down. I will make you a cup of tea," I say as I desperately attempt not to make eye contact. It's the best I could think of on the spot.

"Oh, so just because it is my time of the month, you think I can't make a cup of twatting tea?" she replies.

I am cornered, there is nothing I can say now to improve my situation. But, the idiot that I am, I reply.

"No, I just meant you should sit down and relax. I'll do it," I say this just as the kettle boils.

Wife completely ignores me and proceeds to make me a cup of tea in a manner that befits her mood. After stirring my tea so ferociously that I feared the cup would break, she presents me with my brew, by virtually dropping it on the table in front of me, and splashing scalding hot tea on my hand.

I thought I saw her pupils dilate with pleasure as I desperately hold my scream inside, and I try to look appreciative.

The "tea" she has made me resembles the water you see on TV pumped out of wells in Uganda.

"Thank you," I say while trying to stop the tears that have welled in my eyes from falling.

"Don't be so fucking patronising," Wife shrieks. I am truly fucked now.

"Toast?" she asks while now brandishing a butter knife. I have never felt fearful of a butter knife before, but in the hands of Wife, it now resembles a Machete.

I don't know what to say, but I have to go with it. The alternative was to try and explain to the paramedics how a butter knife ended up embedded in my neck.

"Yes, please," I reluctantly and quietly respond while sipping my hot Ugandan Well water.

After a few minutes, I am presented with my "toast". Now, my toast that I am expected to eat looks like it has been pulled out of a burning building by a fire fighter.

If I had known my toast's next of kin, I would have called them to tell them to come quickly to say their goodbyes, and to bring a priest to perform the last rites.

But, without hesitation with Wife glaring at me, I apply the butter to my toast. I have never heard butter sizzle before when trying to spread it.

I bite down on my toast, and my first bite disintegrates in my mouth. It is like trying to eat charcoal, but with my survival at stake, and Wife wanting me to complain, I eat it all.

I have survived (for now) our breakfast encounter, and I plan to give Wife as wide a berth as possible until Lucifer has left the building.

But, the life of a husband is never predictable. So, I decide to go on a charm offensive. My plan is to try and survive the coming days by showering wife with care and attention in the hope my scrotum will get through this unscathed.

So, for step one, I refill Wife's hot water bottle and I coax her like a lion tamer (minus the whip) to the couch where I place her under a duvet to watch endless hours of mind-numbing sickly-sweet TV shows.

This wasn't an easy task, I had to keep her at arm's length as I suffered volleys of swearing and abuse while guiding her to the couch.

Now Wife has calmed down enough to stop telling me how lucky I am to be male (yeah I am having a whale of a time), I plan my next move. There is only one thing that can contain this demonic possession, and has the power to prevent Wife from turning into Cathy Bates from Stephen King's *Misery*.

It is chocolate.

Yes, Wife will consume so much chocolate in the coming days that if you melted what she eats, you could coat everyone in Belgium.

I honestly don't think the Mayans ever envisaged that

when they first sipped their ceremonial drink containing Cacao beans three thousand years ago, that their discovery would be used to preserve the life of husbands across the world, and suppress Wife's urge to castrate.

So with Wife restrained on the couch, and my genitalia at a safe distance, I inform her of my trip to the shop.

"I am going to the shop for you, what do you wan…" Before I can complete my sentence, Wife butts in.

"Chocolate!" A predictable response to say the least.

So with my shopping list of chocolate in hand, I head out. I thought it was very apt that Meatloaf's "Bat out of Hell" was playing in the kitchen as I make my escape.

It was cold and frosty day, so as you can imagine, I was glad to return from the shop. I was also looking forward to warming up. For a moment, I did contemplate living in the car until Lucifer had left, but four days sat in the car would look odd to the neighbours.

Also, after factoring in the potential dehydration, and hunger, I decide to go inside. So, armed with enough chocolate to hopefully suppress Wife's urges to kill me, I head in.

As I open the door, I am hit with a wall of heat so intense, that as I look down the hall I could see the couch shimmering with heat haze. It was like looking down a Nevada highway in the summer.

Wife had cranked the heating up so high, that I swear I saw an Iguana crawl behind the fridge. The dogs were on their backs with their tongues hanging out the side of their mouths.

After giving the dogs some lifesaving water and

opening the windows to release the inferno of heat, I thought it was fitting that "Devil Woman" by Cliff Richard was now playing on the kitchen radio.

So, with chocolate in hand, I make my way to the lounge with Cliff belting out the lyric "She's a Devil Woman, with Evil on her mind".

I pass the plank sized Cadburys Dairy milk to Wife at arm's length while making sure there was no eye contact. No words were exchanged as Wife tore the plank sized chocolate bar from my grasp, an proceeded to inhale it.

I have never witnessed such ferocity while eating. I left Wife to it, with fragments of chocolate flying everywhere.

I retreated to the kitchen, and to relative safety (at least for my cock) and made myself a cup of tea. I sat there wondering how I was going to make it through the next four days.

While sipping my first proper brew of the day, and planning my strategy, I couldn't believe my ears.

The radio was playing Phil Collins again thanks to a fan who had called in to request the same track I was subjected to this morning!

So, as Phil belted out the chorus "It's just another day for you and me in paradise" I knew that Phil never had to come up against Lucifer for five days every month.

So, as you can tell I did make it through the next four days, because you are reading this. My scrotum is intact, and Wife does not want to kill me, for now.

I could've documented all of what happened in the next four days, but due to actually liking being married to Wife, I thought it best to keep it from the page.

Needless to say, I will probably feel the need to come back to this subject at some point in the future, because unlike all my other accounts so far, this is the only one guaranteed to take place twelve times a year.

So, husbands out there, keep your chocolate supply high, your duvets at the ready, her hot water bottle hot, your eyes down, your ball sack covered, and you might, just might, survive.

# Date with the Devil

As a husband, there are certain dates on your calendar that are important, and there are others that are critical to your survival.

For instance, an important date would be remembering bin day, when to book the car in for its service, not forgetting your dental check-up, and remembering to pay the window cleaner (robbing bastard – see chapter 9 Baby Oil Blues, you'll understand).

Now, forgetting any of these dates may lead to a slight disruption or may inconvenience you a tad, but there are a set of dates that are of such importance that forgetting any of them once, will result in your balls being liberated from their protective sack, and put on display at the Tate Modern.

I am of course referring to any of the following critical dates…

**Anniversary** – This marks the day I walked down the aisle and my soul was sold to Wife. Looking back, the signs were there. The Holy man that bound us in matrimony did look concerned when the holy water began to boil and his crucifix spontaneously combusted. When exchanging vows, the red glow in Wife's eyes was very distracting.

**Valentine's Day** – The day couples over the world mark their love for one another. Little did Emperor

Claudius II realise that when he slaughtered Valentine in the third century, his martyrdom would result in annual slaughtering of husbands over the world for forgetting this sacred date.

In Emperor Claudius' defence, if Valentine was alive today, I would too take great pleasure in slaughtering Valentine. But unlike dying by Claudius's sword, I would insert two dozen red roses inside Valentine, carve a love heart into his chest, coat him in glitter and then finish him off by suffocating him with the three foot teddy bear I bought Wife last year.

Finally, I would display Valentine outside the nearest Card Shop for all to see.

**OK, time out. Now, while reading this next critical date, I want you to be listening to O~Fortuna~ Carmina Burana in the background.**

**Don't let me down, just Google it and press play. It is the only way to truly appreciate the gravity of this date.**

**Right, now that the music is playing read on...**

**Wife's Birthday** – The day the world changed forever. This marks the day that Wife arrived on Planet Earth. Some say that the sun was blood red on this day, the birds ceased their song and the rivers ran red with the blood of the innocent.

Others say it was a wet Tuesday in Preston. Nevertheless, this was the day that Wife arrived.

On this day, every year, I pay homage to Wife in the form of financial buggery, reconfirming my status as a slave, and constantly praising and reassuring Wife that she looks the same as the day we met.

Of course, between you and me, neither Wife nor I look anything like the day we met. If you had shown me a picture of us today, from when we first met, I would've thought it was one of those pictures of someone you see showing them before and after they spent years on Crystal Meth.

Mick Jagger probably really believed that time was indeed on his side when he sang "Time is on my side" in 1964, because he was twenty-one years old.

I bet he doesn't think it today. There lies the truth, time waits for no man (or wife), and I have come to peace with that.

Don't get me wrong, I am not old (well, not that old) but with age comes contentment and acceptance that I am never going to look like twenty-one-year-old me ever again. And that's OK.

Mind you, seventy-three-year-old Mick Jagger can still move better than I can at nearly half his age.

Fuck you Mick.

**Oh, I meant to say earlier you can stop listening to the music now. That last passage of relative sentiment probably sounded a bit weird against the backdrop of biblical opera.**

So husbands, I have outlined the three most important dates in your calendar that you must never ever forget, for the sake of your testicles and your desire to not sleep in the car.

Now, before I begin my account, There is one thing I need to cover that is not quite as bad as forgetting any of these critical dates, but can (and probably will) result in you being deprived of sex for so long, that the next time

Wife flashes her ankle, it will result in a very messy accident in your pants.

This is of course "remembering at the last minute". Now, you may think, "thank god, I remembered" and you would be right, but it is seven forty-five p.m. the night before her birthday, and panic sets in.

What do you do? Well, there are only two ways out of this, and one is only slightly better than the other.

1, You make up a shitty excuse for having to go out, and embark on a mission to get Wife's birthday gifts, in the hope of her never finding out you had forgotten.

This is a difficult strategy as it is nearly eight p.m., and the only places open are supermarkets and petrol stations. So, get it wrong, and your "gifts" will scream last minute, and that you had forgotten.

There will be countless wives up and down the lands wearing earrings on her birthday, fashioned out of husbands testicles, because that morning she received, a pine scented air freshener for her car, a copy of the good housekeeping magazine, a large can of De-Icer and a lottery scratch card.

Oh, and not forgetting a hastily gathered bunch of Daffodil's from a roundabout, and a voucher for five pence a litre off her next fill up.

The second option is…

2, You pretend you have not forgotten. This involves telling Wife on the morning of her birthday that her present is a surprise, and that she will receive it at some point on her birthday.

This is a risky strategy, as Wife can stare into your soul and read the truth. So eye contact must be kept to a minimum.

The other problem with this approach is that Wife will be with you for most of the day, and it is nigh on impossible to escape her gaze (Wife's stare is like the Dark Lord Sauron's eye from "Lord of the Rings", lidless and wreathed in flame, ever watching, never sleeping), so getting any opportunity to escape to obtain Wife's present is very difficult.

Get this wrong, and believe me, you would rather face all the goblin armies of Mordor (sorry, Lord of the Rings fan here) than stand before Wife at the end of her birthday, with her flaring nostrils, and no gifts to honour her.

I am going to give you a strategy here that can literally save you from being skinned alive.

If you awaken and realise it is Wife's birthday, and you have forgotten, listen very carefully.

Firstly, DO NOT TELL THE TRUTH!

Any element of "I forgot" or "I am sorry" will be met with a response akin to a drop of blood landing in the ocean within five hundred metres of a nineteen foot Great White Shark.

What you need to do first is stay calm. When Wife wakes on her birthday, be proactive, let me demonstrate. Listen and follow this to the letter…

Firstly you must say, "Good morning, birthday girl. Happy birthday! I love you!" Give her a kiss. You have taken the lead, and she suspects nothing.

Then as she realises there are no gifts in the room, again, take the lead…

Say this before she can ask about the lack of presents.

"I can't wait to give you your present." Again, you have the initiative.

She will ask, "What is it?" A predictable response.

Again, stay calm, and say casually, "It's a surprise, I thought I would do something different this year." She thinks you have planned something different because you care, not because you are a forgetful twat.

Now, you have bought yourself time.

So, what you then do is take Wife out for a birthday lunch. Predictable? Well yes, but this next part will mean you can rescue the day.

The key here is to choose a restaurant that is in town, and somewhere a little more expensive than you would normally choose (I hear you sighing from here, but I didn't say it would be a cheap solution, just one that will keep your penis intact) and crucially, within two hundred metres of a jewellers.

So, on arrival at the restaurant she will be impressed, and your standing with her is slightly elevated. Now, after the first course, you must excuse yourself and tell her you need to visit the men's room.

Now, sprint as fast as you can to the jewellers, explain as quickly as possible to the jeweller that you have forgotten Wife's birthday, and tell him that after your lunch you will be bringing Wife in to choose her present.

Then tell the jeweller Wife's name, and ask her for a gift card, fill out the gift card and ask the jeweller to keep hold of it until you return.

Finally, tell the jeweller to only show Wife items up to £200 when she comes in.

Now sprint back the restaurant, to enjoy he rest of your rather pricey lunch.

Upon leaving the restaurant, guide Wife to the jewellers and enter. When Wife enters she is greeted by the lady who uses Wife's name and wishes her happy birthday (Wife is impressed and thinks this took a lot of planning).

The lady hands Wife the gift card I wrote about an hour ago, wishing her a happy birthday and saying she can choose what she likes.

Upon previous instructions, the lady shows Wife only the items up to £200 (although Wife thinks she has free reign of the shop).

Wife proceeds to choose her necklace, and she is very happy.

Your life has been saved. Your wallet isn't suffering too much, Wife thinks you are as charming as James Bond, the only downside was a slight asthma attack you suffered after sprinting to the jewellers.

BOOM! Husbands, you can have that one on me. But, remember that you will only be able to get away with this once, so be warned.

So after my pearl of wisdom gift to you, I will move to my account of Wife's birthday, and what occurred.

So the day before Wife's birthday I set out my plan. I have been married to Wife long enough now to know forgetting her birthday is not an option, and to be honest, her hints in the weeks leading up to the momentous day are anything but subtle.

In fact, residents at Guantanamo Bay have experienced more subtlety when choking on engine oil during interrogation.

So, with an already purchased set of earrings stashed under my condom supply (which has a disturbing amount of dust on it) , an impressively large bunch of flowers in water in the garage (in the bucket I had to use to relieve myself in when Wife locked me out of the house – she made me sleep in the garage after coming back at four a.m. from my fancy dress work do, blind drunk, dressed as Shrek).

All that is left to acquire is a birthday card. Now, this is a relatively simple task for me (and most husbands, I think) but for Wife (and women in general) it is a monumental task, they spend copious amounts of time choosing a card.

In fact, I now know why they have a display of lady razors at the end of the card displays. It is due to the fact that by the time Wife has chosen a card, her smooth legs now resemble that of a Chimpanzee.

Now as I arrive at the card shop, one thing is guaranteed. Let me explain the scene, the entire shop is littered with women transfixed and reading verse after verse on various cards. They are pondering which card to choose for their recipient, who like me, unless there is money in a card or naked breasts, couldn't care less what it said.

Card shops are confusing places, so after circumnavigating many stationary females, I find the wife section.

I spend twenty seconds choosing a card in an acceptable form, and narrowly miss purchasing a "Sorry for your loss card" which was mistakenly in the birthday section.

Another thing about card shops is there is always a female shop assistant on her knees, frantically sorting out the cards to keep them meticulously in order.

These ladies watch you like a hawk to make sure you do not put any card back in the wrong section. I often wondered what would happen if I did misplace a card.

It would probably result in the alarm sounding, the shutters falling and the red sirens going off. I would undoubtedly be apprehended and led to the basement, where I would be subjected to paper cuts between my toes using a happy vasectomy day card.

So, with card in hand, making sure it had the key words "Wife" and "Birthday", I pay the extortionate fee to own this card, and leave the stationary women to agonise over their card choices. I actually brush past a lady on the way out just to make sure she is not made of cardboard.

Upon my return, Wife is suspicious.

"Where have you been?" she enquires.

"Oh, just for a stroll," I say smugly. She knows by now that surely, I would not leave anything to chance.

Needless to say, her birthday passed smoothly, and she loved her earrings. Unlike other accounts you have read so far, there was no drama, no calamity and as far as Wife was concerned I didn't need to sleep in the garage with my bucket.

The moral of this account is preparation is everything. But, this only comes with experience. So to all new husbands out there that need guidance, by all means use the Jewellery/Lunch method to save you, but remember this will only save you once.

So, in all honesty, if you make the same mistake twice, remember…

"Hell hath no fury like a woman scorned," William Congreve, 1697.

You are on your own!